A Treasury of Wisdom

ISBN: 1 84013 379 1

Reprinted 2003

This edition produced for Grange Books
Units 1-6 Kingsnorth Ind.Est.
Hoo, Nr. Rochester
Kent ME3 9ND
United Kingdom
www.grangebooks.co.uk

GRANGE BOOKS PLC

A Treasury of Wisdom

A Collection of the
Works of Kahlil Gibran

GRANGE BOOKS PLC

Contents

GOD'S FOOL 7
GARMENTS 10
THE HERMIT PROPHET 11
THE OLD, OLD WINE 12
THE KING 13
THE POMEGRANATES 16
WAR AND THE SMALL NATIONS 17
THE PLUTOCRAT 18
THE SAINT 19
BEYOND MY SOLITUDE 20
REPENTANCE 21
KNOWLEDGE AND HALF-KNOWLEDGE 22
VALUES 23
A POET'S DEATH IS HIS LIFE 24
THE EYE 26
THE FOX 27
THE SLEEP-WALKERS 28
THE WISE DOG 29
THE NEW PLEASURE 30
THE THREE ANTS 31
TWO INFANTS 32
THE WIDOW AND HER SON 34
LAUGHTER AND TEARS 36
YESTERDAY AND TODAY 39
THE MERMAIDS 42
SECRETS OF THE HEART 45
NATURE AND MAN 49
YOUTH AND HOPE 51
MY SOUL PREACHED TO ME 55
SEVEN REPRIMANDS 59
VISION 60

O SOUL 62
HANDFUL OF BEACH SAND 63
SOLITUDE AND SECLUSION 65
THE SONS OF THE GODDESS
AND THE SONS OF THE MONKEYS 67
THE TWO HUNTERS 70
THE QUEST 71
LOVE AND HATE 72
THE MADMAN 73
THE STATUE 74
THE TWO GUARDIAN ANGELS 75
THE TWO LEARNED MEN 77
THE GOOD GOD AND THE EVIL GOD 78
THE LOVE SONG 79
THE THREE GIFTS 80
PEACE AND WAR 81
TEARS AND LAUGHTER 82
AT THE FAIR 83
THE SPEECHLESS ANIMAL 84
COMMUNION OF SPIRITS 86
WISDOM AND I 89
LOVE AND YOUTH 92
THE LISTENER 94
FACES 97
THE HERMIT AND THE BEASTS 98
THE SHADOW 99
THE CRIMINAL 100
THE PATH 102
THE SEVEN SELVES 104
THE GREATER SEA 106
THE WHITE TORCH 108
THE POET 111
THE TEMPEST 114

GOD'S FOOL

Once there came from the desert to the great city of Sharia a man who was a dreamer, and he had naught but his garment and a staff.

And as he walked through the streets he gazed with awe and wonder at the temples and towers and palaces, for the city of Sharia was of surpassing beauty. And he spoke often to the passers-by, questioning them about their city—but they understood not his language, nor he their language.

At the noon hour he stopped before a vast inn. It was built of yellow marble, and people were going in and coming out unhindered.

"This must be a shrine," he said to himself, and he too went in. But what was his surprise to find himself in a hall of great splendour and a large company of men and women seated about many tables. They were eating and drinking and listening to the musicians.

"Nay," said the dreamer. "This is no worshipping. It must be a feast given by the prince to the people, in celebration of a great event."

At that moment a man, whom he took to be the slave of the prince, approached him, and bade him be seated. And he was served with meat and wine and most excellent sweets.

When he was satisfied, the dreamer rose to depart. At the door he was stopped by a large man magnificently arrayed.

"Surely this is the prince himself," said the dreamer in his heat, and he bowed to him and thanked him.

Then the large man said in the language of the city:

"Sir, you have not paid for your dinner." And the dreamer did not understand, and again thanked him heartily. Then the large man bethought him, and he looked more closely upon the dreamer. And he saw that he was a stranger, clad in but a poor garment, and that indeed he had not wherewith to pay for his meal. Then the large man clapped his hands and called—and there came four watchmen of the city. And they listened to the large man. Then they took the dreamer between them, and they were two on each side of him. And the dreamer noted the ceremoniousness of their dress and of their manner and he looked upon them with delight.

"These," said he, "are men of distinction."

And they walked all together until they came to the House of Judgment and they entered.

The dreamer saw before him, seated upon a throne, a venerable man with flowing beard, robed majestically. And he thought he was the king. And he rejoiced to be brought before him.

Now the watchmen related to the judge, who was the venerable man, the charge against the dreamer; and the judge appointed two advocates, one to present the charge and the other to defend the stranger. And the advocates rose, the one after other, and delivered each his argument. And the dreamer thought himself to be listening to addresses of welcome, and his heart filled with gratitude to the king and the prince for all that was done for him.

Then sentence was passed upon the dreamer, that upon a tablet hung about his neck his crime should be written, and that he should ride through the city on a naked horse, with a trumpeter and a drummer before him. And the sentence was carried out forthwith.

Now as the dreamer rode through the city upon the naked horse, with the trumpeter and the drummer before him, the inhabitants of the city came running forth at the sound of the noise, and when they saw him they laughed one and all, and the children ran after him in companies from street to street. And the dreamer's heart filled with ecstasy, and his eyes shone upon them. For to him the tablet was a sign of the king's blessing and the procession was in his honour.

Now as he rode, he saw among the crowd a man who was from the desert like himself and his heart swelled with joy, and he cried out to him with a shout:

"Friend! Friend! Where are we? What city of the heart's desire is this? What race of lavish hosts?—who feast the chance guest in their palaces, whose princes companion him, whose king hangs a token upon his breast and opens to him the hospitality of a city descended from heaven."

And he who was also of the desert replied not. He only smiled and slightly shook his head. And the procession passed on.

And the dreamer's face was uplifted and his eyes were overflowing with light.

GARMENTS

Upon a day Beauty and Ugliness met on the shore of a sea. And they said to one another, "Let us bathe in the sea."

Then they disrobed and swam in the waters. And after a while Ugliness came back to shore and garmented himself with the garments of Beauty and walked his way.

And Beauty too came out of the sea, and found not her raiment, and she was too shy to be naked, therefore she dressed herself with the raiment of Ugliness. And Beauty walked her way.

And to this very day men and women mistake the one for the other.

Yet some there are who have beheld the face of Beauty, and they know her notwithstanding her garments. And some there be who know the face of Ugliness, and the cloth conceals him not from their eyes.

THE HERMIT PROPHET

Once there lived a hermit prophet, and thrice a moon he would go down to the great city and in the market places he would preach giving and sharing to the people. And he was eloquent, and his fame was upon the land.

Upon an evening three men came to his hermitage and he greeted them. And they said, "You have been preaching giving and sharing, and you have sought to teach those who have much to give unto those who have little; and we doubt not that your fame has brought you riches. Now come and give us of your riches, for we are in need."

And the hermit answered and said, "My friends, I have naught but this bed and this mat and this jug of water. Take them if it is in your desire. I have neither gold nor silver."

Then they looked down with disdain upon him, and turned their faces from him; and the last man stood at the door for a moment, and said, "Oh, you cheat! You fraud! You teach and preach that which you yourself do not perform."

THE OLD, OLD WINE

Once there lived a rich man who was justly proud of his cellar and the wine therein. And there was one jug of ancient vintage kept for some occasion known only to himself.

The governor of the state visited him, and he bethought him and said, "That jug shall not be opened for a mere governor."

And a bishop of the diocese visited him, but he said to himself, "Nay, I will not open that jug. He would not know its value, nor would its aroma reach his nostrils."

The prince of the realm came and supped with him. But he thought, "It is too royal a wine for a mere princeling."

And even on the day when his own nephew was married, he said to himself, "No, not to these guests shall that jug be brought forth."

And the years passed by, and he died, an old man, and he was buried like unto every seed and acorn.

And upon the day that he was buried the ancient jug was brought out together with other jugs of wine, and it was shared by the peasants of the neighbourhood. And none knew its great age.

To them, all that is poured into a cup is only wine.

THE KING

The people of the Kingdom of Sadik surrounded the palace of their king shouting in rebellion against him. And he came down the steps of the palace carrying his crown in one hand and his sceptre in the other. The majesty of his appearance silenced the multitude, and he stood before them and said, "My friends, who are no longer my subjects, here I yield my crown and sceptre unto you. I would be one of you. I am only one man, but as a man I would work together with you that our lot may be made better. There is no need for a king. Let us go therefore to the fields and the vineyards and labour hand with hand. Only you must tell me to what field or vineyard I should go. All of you now are king."

And the people marvelled, and stillness was upon them, for the king whom they had deemed the source of their discontent now yielded his crown and sceptre to them and became as one of them.

Then each and every one of them went his way, and the king walked with one man to a field.

But the Kingdom of Sadik fared not better without a king, and the mist of discontent was still upon the land. The people cried out in the market places saying that they would be governed, and that they would have a king to rule them. And the elders and the youths said as if with one voice, "We will have our king."

And they sought the king and found him toiling in the field, and they brought him to his seat, and yielded unto him his crown and his sceptre. And they said, "Now rule us, with might and with justice."

And he said, "I will indeed rule you with might, and may the gods of the heaven and the earth help me that I may also rule with justice."

Now, there came to his presence men and women and spoke unto him of a baron who mistreated them, and to whom they were but serfs. And straightway the king brought the baron before him and said, "The life of one man is as weighty in the scales of God as the life of another. And because you know not how to weigh the lives of those who work in your fields and your vineyards, you are banished, and you shall leave this kingdom forever."

The following day came another company to the king and spoke of the cruelty of a countess beyond the hills, and how she brought them down to misery. Instantly the countess was brought to court, and the king sentenced her also to banishment, saying, "Those who till our fields and care for our vineyards are nobler than we who eat the bread they prepare and drink the wine of their wine-press. And because you know not this, you shall leave this land and be afar from this kingdom."

Then came men and women who said that the bishop made them bring stones and hew the stones for the cathedral, yet he gave them naught, though they knew the bishop's coffer was full of gold and silver while they themselves were empty with hunger.

And the king called for the bishop and when the bishop came the king spoke and said unto him, "That cross you wear upon your bosom should mean giving life unto life. But you have taken life from life and you have given none. Therefore you shall leave this kingdom never to return."

Thus each day for a full moon men and women came to

the king to tell him of the burdens laid upon them. And each and every day for a full moon some oppressor was exiled from the land.

And the people of Sadik were amazed, and there was cheer in their heart.

And upon a day the elders and the youths came and surrounded the tower of the king and called for him. And he came down holding his crown with one hand and his sceptre with the other.

And he spoke unto them and said, "Now, what would you of me? Behold, I yield back to you that which you desired me to hold."

But they cried, "Nay, nay, you are our rightful king. You have made clean the land of vipers, and you have brought the wolves to naught, and we come to sing our thanksgiving unto you. The crown is yours in majesty and the sceptre is yours in glory."

Then the king said, "Not I, not I. You yourselves are king. When you deemed me weak and a misruler, you yourselves were weak and misruling. And now the land fares well because it is in your will. I am but a thought in the mind of you all, and I exist not save in your actions. There is no such person as governor. Only the governed exist to govern themselves."

And the king re-entered his tower with his crown and his sceptre. And the elders and the youths went their various ways and they were content.

And each and every one thought of himself as king with a crown in one hand and a sceptre in the other.

THE POMEGRANATES

There was once a man who had many pomegranate trees in his orchard. And for many an autumn he would put his pomegranates on silvery trays outside of his dwelling, and upon the trays he would place signs upon which he himself had written, "Take one for aught. You are welcome."

But people passed by and no one took of the fruit.

Then the man bethought him, and one autumn he places no pomegranates on silvery trays outside of his dwelling, but he raised this sign in large lettering: "Here we have the best pomegranates in the land, but we sell them for more silver than any other pomegranates."

And now behold, all the men and women of the neighbourhood came rushing to buy.

WAR AND THE SMALL NATIONS

Once, high above a pasture, where a sheep and a lamb were grazing, an eagle was circling and gazing hungrily down upon the lamb. And as he was about to descend and seize his prey, another eagle appeared and hovered above the sheep and her young with the same hungry intent. Then the two rivals began to fight filling the sky with their fierce cries.

The sheep looked up and was much astonished. She turned to the lamb and said, "How strange, my child, that these two noble birds should attack one another. Is not the vast sky large enough for both of them? Pray, my little one, pray in your heart that God may make peace between your winged brothers."

And the lamb prayed in his heart.

THE PLUTOCRAT

In my wanderings I once saw upon an island a man-headed, iron-hoofed monster who ate of the earth and drank of the sea incessantly. And for a long while I watched him. Then I approached him and said, "Have you never enough; is your hunger never satisfied and your thirst never quenched?"

And he answered saying, "Yes, I am satisfied, nay, I am weary of eating and drinking; but I am afraid that tomorrow there will be no more earth to eat and no more sea to drink."

THE SAINT

In my youth I once visited a saint in his silent grove beyond the hills; and as we were conversing upon the nature of virtue a brigand came limping wearily up the ridge. When he reached the grove he knelt down before the saint and said, "O saint, I would be comforted! My sins are heavy upon me."

And the saint replied, "My sins, too, are heavy upon me."

And the brigand said, "But I am a thief and a plunderer."

And the saint replied, "I too am a thief and a plunderer."

And the brigand said, "But I am a murderer, and the blood of many men cries in my ears."

And the saint replied, "I too am a murderer, and in my ears cries the blood of many men."

And the brigand said, "I have committed countless crimes."

And the saint replied, "I too have committed crimes without number."

Then the brigand stood up and gazed at the saint, and there was a strange look in his eyes. And when he left us he went skipping down the hill.

And I turned to the saint and said, "Wherefore did you accuse yourself of uncommitted crimes? See you not that this man went away no longer believing in you?"

And the saint answered, "It is true he no longer believes in me. But he went away much comforted."

At that moment we heard the brigand singing in the distance, and the echo of his song filled the valley with gladness.

BEYOND MY SOLITUDE

Beyond my solitude is another solitude, and to him who dwells therein my aloneness is a crowded market-place and my silence a confusion of sounds.

Too young am I and too restless to seek that above solitude. The voices of yonder valley still hold my ears, and its shadows bar my way and I cannot go.

Beyond these hills is a grove of enchantment and to him who dwells therein my peace is but a whirlwind and my enchantment an illusion.

Too young am I and too riotous to seek that sacred grove. The taste of blood is clinging in my mouth, and the bow and the arrows of my fathers yet linger in my hand and I cannot go.

Beyond this burdened self lives my freer self; and to him my dreams are a battle fought in twilight and my desires the rattling of bones.

Too young am I and too outraged to be my freer self.

And how shall I become my freer self unless I slay my burdened selves, or unless all men become free?

How shall my leaves fly singing upon the wind unless my roots shall wither in the dark?

How shall the eagle in me soar against the sun until my fledglings leave the nest which I with my own beak have built for them?

REPENTANCE

On a moonless night a man entered into his neighbour's garden and stole the largest melon he could find and brought it home.

He opened it and found it still unripe.

Then behold a marvel!

The man's conscience woke and smote him with remorse; and he repented having stolen the melon.

KNOWLEDGE AND HALF-KNOWLEDGE

Four frogs sat upon a log that lay floating on the edge of a river. Suddenly the log was caught by the current and swept slowly down the stream. The frogs were delighted and absorbed, for never before had they sailed.

At length the first frog spoke, and said, "This is indeed a most marvellous log. It moves as if alive. No such log was ever known before."

Then the second frog spoke, and said, "Nay, my friend, the log is like other logs, and does not move. It is the river, that is walking to the sea, and carries us and the log with it."

And the third frog spoke, and said, "It is neither the log nor the river that moves. The moving is in our thinking. For without thought nothing moves."

And the three frogs began to wrangle about what was really moving. The quarrel grew hotter and louder, but they could not agree.

Then they turned to the fourth frog, who up to this time had been listening attentively but holding his peace, and they asked his opinion.

And the fourth frog said, "Each of you is right, and none of you is wrong. The moving is in the log and the water and our thinking also."

And the three frogs became very angry, for none of them was willing to admit that his was not the whole truth, and that the other two were not wholly wrong.

Then the strange thing happened. The three frogs got together and pushed the fourth frog off the log into the river.

VALUES

Once a man unearthed in his field a marble statue of great beauty. And he took it to a collector who loved all beautiful things and offered it to him for sale, and the collector bought it for a large price. And they parted.

And as the man walked home with his money he thought, and he said to himself, "How much life this money means! How can any one give all this for a dead carved stone buried and undreamed of in the earth for a thousand years?"

And now the collector was looking at his statue, and he was thinking, and he said to himself, "What beauty! What life! The dream of what a soul!—How can any one give all this for money, dead and dreamless?"

A POET'S DEATH IS HIS LIFE

The dark wings of night enfolded the city upon which Nature had spread a pure and white garment of snow; and men deserted the streets for their houses in search of warmth, while the north wind probed in contemplation of laying waste the gardens. There in the suburb stood an old hut heavily laden with snow and on the verge of falling. In a dark recess of that hovel was a poor bed in which a dying youth was lying, staring at the dim light of his oil lamp, made to flicker by the entering winds. He was a man in the spring of life who foresaw fully that the peaceful hour of freeing himself from the clutches of life was fast nearing. He was awaiting Death's visit gratefully, and upon his pale face appeared the dawn of hope; and on his lips a sorrowful smile; and in his eyes forgiveness.

He was a poet perishing from hunger in the city of living rich. He was placed in the earthly world to enliven the heart of man with his beautiful and profound sayings. He was a noble soul, sent by the Goddess of Understanding to soothe and make gentle the human spirit. But alas! He gladly bade the cold earth farewell without receiving a smile from its strange occupants.

He was breathing his last and had no one at his bedside save the oil lamp, his only companion, and some parchments upon which he had inscribed his heart's feeling. As he salvaged the remnants of his withering strength he lifted his hands heavenward; he moved his eyes hopelessly, as if wanting to penetrate the ceiling in order to see the stars from behind the veil of clouds.

And he said, "Come, oh beautiful Death; my soul is

longing for you. Come close to me and unfasten the irons of life, for I am weary of dragging them. Come, oh sweet Death, and deliver me from my neighbours who looked upon me as a stranger because I interpret to them the language of the angels. Hurry, oh peaceful Death, and carry me from these multitudes who left me in the dark corner of oblivion because I do not bleed the weak as they do. Come, oh gentle Death, and enfold me under your white wings, for my fellowmen are not in want of me. Embrace me, oh Death, full of love and mercy; let your lips touch my lips which never tasted a mother's kiss, nor touched a sister's cheeks, nor caressed a sweetheart's fingertips. Come and take me, my beloved Death."

Then, at the bedside of the dying poet appeared an angel who possessed a supernatural and divine beauty, holding in her hand a wreath of lilies. She embraced him and closed his eyes so he could see no more, except with the eye of his spirit. She impressed a deep and long and gently withdrawn kiss that left an eternal smile of fulfilment upon his lips. Then the hovel became empty and nothing was left save parchments and papers which the poet had strewn about with bitter futility.

Hundreds of years later, when the people of the city arose from the diseased slumber of ignorance and saw the dawn of knowledge, they erected a monument in the most beautiful garden of the city and celebrated a feast every year in honour of that poet, whose writings had freed them. Oh, how cruel is man's ignorance!

THE EYE

Said the Eye one day, "I see beyond these valleys a mountain veiled with blue mist. Is it not beautiful?"

The Ear listened, and after listening intently awhile, said, "But where is any mountain? I do not hear it."

Then the Hand spoke and said, "I am trying in vain to feel it or touch it, and I can find no mountain."

And the Nose said, "There is no mountain, I cannot smell it."

Then the Eye turned the other way, and they all began to talk together about the Eye's strange delusion. And they said, "Something must be the matter with the Eye."

THE FOX

A Fox looked at his shadow at sunrise and said, "I will have a camel for lunch today." And all morning he went about looking for camels. But at noon he saw his shadow again—and he said, "A mouse will do."

THE SLEEP-WALKERS

In the town where I was born lived a woman and her daughter, who walked in their sleep.

One night, while silence enfolded the world, the woman and her daughter, walking, yet asleep, met in their mist-veiled garden.

And the mother spoke, and she said: "At last, at last, my enemy! You by whom my youth was destroyed—who have built up your life upon the ruins of mine! Would I could kill you!"

And the daughter spoke, and she said: "O hateful woman, selfish and old! Who stand between my freer self and me! Who would have my life an echo of your own faded life! Would you were dead!"

At that moment a cock crew, and both women awoke. The mother said gently, "Is that you, darling?" And the daughter answered gently, "Yes, dear."

THE WISE DOG

One day there passed by a company of cats a wise dog.

And as he came near and saw that they were very intent and heeded him not, he stopped.

Then there arose in the midst of the company a large, grave cat and looked upon them and said, "Brethren, pray ye; and when ye have prayed again and yet again, nothing doubting, verily then it shall rain mice."

And when the dog heard this he laughed in his heart and turned from them saying, "O blind and foolish cats, has it not been written and have I not known and my fathers before me, that that which raineth for prayer and faith and supplication is not mice but bones."

THE NEW PLEASURE

Last night I invented a new pleasure, and as I was giving it the first trial an angel and a devil came rushing toward my house. They met at my door and fought with each other over my newly created pleasure; the one crying, "It is a sin!"—the other, "It is a virtue!"

THE THREE ANTS

Three ants met on the nose of a man who was lying asleep in the sun. And after they had saluted one another, each according to the custom of his tribe, they stood there conversing.

The first ant said, "These hills and plains are the most barren I have known. I have searched all day for a grain of some sort, and there is none to be found."

Said the second ant, "I too have found nothing, though I have visited every nook and glade. This is, I believe, what my people call the soft, moving land where nothing grows."

Then the third ant raised his head and said, "My friends, we are standing now on the nose of the Supreme Ant, the mighty and infinite Ant, whose body is so great that we cannot see it, whose shadow is so vast that we cannot trace it, whose voice is so loud that we cannot hear it; and He is omnipresent."

When the third ant spoke thus the other ants looked at each other and laughed.

At that moment the man moved and in his sleep raised his hand and scratched his nose, and the three ants were crushed.

TWO INFANTS

A prince stood on the balcony of his palace addressing a great multitude summoned for the occasion and said, "Let me offer you and this whole fortunate country my congratulations upon the birth of a new prince who will carry the name of my noble family, and of whom you will be justly proud. He is the new bearer of a great and illustrious ancestry, and upon him depends the brilliant future of this realm. Sing and be merry!" The voices of the throngs, full of joy and thankfulness, flooded the sky with exhilarating song, welcoming the new tyrant who would affix the yoke of oppression to their necks by ruling the weak with bitter authority, and exploiting their bodies and killing their souls. For that destiny, the people were singing and drinking ecstatically to the health of the new Emir.

Another child entered life and that kingdom at the same time. While the crowds were glorifying the strong and belittling themselves by singing praise to a potential despot, and while the angels of heaven were weeping over the people's weakness and servitude, a sick woman was thinking. She lived in an old, deserted hovel and, lying in her hard bed beside her newly-born infant wrapped with ragged swaddles, was starving to death. She was a penurious and miserable young wife neglected by humanity; her husband had fallen into the trap of death set by the prince's oppression, leaving a solitary woman to whom God had sent, that night, a tiny companion to prevent her from working and sustaining life.

As the mass dispersed and silence was restored to the vicinity, the wretched woman placed the infant on her lap and looked into his face and wept as if she were to baptize him with tears. And with a hunger-weakened voice she spoke to the child saying, "Why have you left the spiritual world and come to share with me the bitterness of earthly life? Why have you deserted the angels and the spacious firmament and come to this miserable land of humans, filled with agony, oppression, and heartlessness? I have nothing to give you except tears; will you be nourished on tears instead of milk? I have no silk clothes to put on you; will my naked, shivering arms give you warmth? The little animals graze in the pasture and return safely to their shed; and the small birds pick the seeds and sleep placidly between the branches. But you, my beloved, have naught save a loving but destitute mother."

Then she took the infant to her withered breast and clasped her arms around him as if wanting to join the two bodies in one, as before. She lifted her burning eyes slowly toward heaven and cried, "God! Have mercy on my unfortunate countrymen!"

At that moment the clouds floated from the face of the moon, whose beams penetrated the transom of that poor home and fell upon two corpses.

THE WIDOW AND HER SON

Night fell over North Lebanon and snow was covering the villages surrounded by the Kadeesha Valley, giving the fields and prairies the appearance of a great sheet of parchment upon which the furious Nature was recording her many deeds. Men came home from the streets while silence engulfed the night.

In a lone house near those villages lived a woman who sat by her fireside spinning wool, and at her side was her only child, staring now at the fire and then at his mother.

A terrible roar of thunder shook the house and the little boy took fright. He threw his arms about his mother, seeking protection from Nature in her affection. She took him on her lap and said, "Do not fear, my son, for Nature is but comparing her great power to man's weakness, There is a Supreme Being beyond the falling snow and the heavy clouds and the blowing wind, and He knows the needs of the earth, for He made it; and He looks upon the weak with merciful eyes.

"Be brave, my boy. Nature smiles in Spring and laughs in Summer and yawns in Autumn, but now she is weeping; and with her tears she waters life, hidden under the earth.

"Sleep, my dear child; your father is viewing us from Eternity. The snow and thunder bring us closer to him at this time.

"Sleep, my beloved, for this white blanket which make us cold, keeps the seeds warm, and these warlike things will produce beautiful flowers when Nisan comes.

"Thus, my child, man cannot reap love until after sad and

revealing separation, and bitter patience, and desperate hardship. Sleep, my little boy; sweet dreams will find your soul who is unafraid of the terrible darkness of night and the biting frost."

The little boy looked upon his mother with sleep-laden eyes and said, "Mother, my eyes are heavy, but I cannot go to sleep without saying my prayer."

The woman looked at his angelic face, her vision blurred by misted eyes, and said, "Repeat with me, my boy—'God, have mercy on the poor and protect them from the winter; warm their thin-clad bodies with Thy merciful hands; look upon the orphans who are sleeping in wretched houses, suffering from hunger and cold. Hear, oh Lord, the call of widows who are helpless and shivering with fear for their young. Open, oh Lord, the hearts of all humans, that they may see the misery of the weak. Have mercy upon the sufferers who knock on doors, and lead the wayfarers into warm places. Watch, oh Lord, over the little birds and protect the trees and fields from the anger of the storm; for Thou art merciful and full of love."

As Slumber captured the boy's spirit, his mother placed him in the bed and kissed his eyes with quivering lips. Then she went back and sat by the hearth, spinning the wool to make him raiment.

LAUGHTER AND TEARS

As the sun withdrew his rays from the garden, and the moon threw cushioned beams upon the flowers, I sat under the trees pondering upon the phenomena of the atmosphere, looking through the branches at the strewn stars which glittered like chips of silver upon a blue carpet; and I could hear from a distance the agitated murmur of the rivulet singing its way briskly into the valley.

When the birds took shelter among the boughs, and the flowers folded their petals, and tremendous silence descended, I heard a rustle of feet through the grass. I took heed and saw a young couple approaching my arbor. They sat under a tree where I could see them without being seen.

After he looked about in every direction, I heard the young man saying, "Sit by me, my beloved, and listen to my heart; smile, for your happiness is a symbol of our future; be merry, for the sparkling days rejoice with us.

"My soul is warning me of the doubt in your heart, for doubt in love is a sin.

"Soon you will be the owner of this vast land, lighted by this beautiful moon; soon you will be the mistress of my palace, and all the servants and maids will obey your commands.

"Smile, my beloved, like the gold smiles from my father's coffers.

"My heart refuses to deny you its secret. Twelve months of comfort and travel await us; for a year we will spend my father's gold at the blue lakes of Switzerland, and viewing the edifices of Italy and Egypt, and resting under the Holy

Cedars of Lebanon; you will meet the princesses who will envy you for your jewels and clothes.

"All these things I will do for you; will you be satisfied?"

In a little while I saw them walking and stepping on flowers as the rich step upon the hearts of the poor. As they disappeared from my sight, I commenced to make comparison between love and money, and to analyse their position in my heart.

Money! The source of insincere love; the spring of false light and fortune; the well of poisoned water; the desperation of old age!

I was still wandering in the vast desert of contemplation when a forlorn and spectre-like couple passed by me and sat on the grass; a young man and a young woman who had left their farming shacks in the nearby fields for this cool and solitary place.

After a few moments of complete silence, I heard the following words uttered with sighs from weather-bitten lips, "Shed not tears, my beloved; love that opens our eyes and enslaves our hearts, can give us the blessings of patience. Be consoled in our delay, for we have taken an oath and entered Love's shrine for our love will ever grow in adversity; for it is in Love's name that we are suffering the obstacles of poverty and the sharpness of misery and the emptiness of separation. I shall attack these hardships until I triumph and place in your hands a strength that will help over all things to complete the journey of life.

"Love—which is God—will consider our sighs and tears as incense burned at His alter and He will reward us with fortitude. Good-bye, my beloved; I must leave before the heartening moon vanishes."

A pure voice, combined of the consuming flame of love, and the hopeless bitterness of longing and the resolved sweetness of patience, said, "Good-bye, my beloved."

They separated, and the elegy to their union was smothered by the wails of my crying heart.

I looked upon slumbering Nature, and with deep reflection discovered the reality of a vast and infinite thing— something no power could demand, influence acquire, nor riches purchase. Nor could it be effaced by the tears of time or deadened by sorrow; a thing which cannot be discovered by the blue lakes of Switzerland or the beautiful edifices of Italy.

It is something that gathers strength with patience, grows despite obstacles, warms in winter, flourishes in spring, casts a breeze in summer, and bears fruit in autumn—I found Love.

YESTERDAY AND TODAY

The gold-hoarder walked in his palace park and with him walked his troubles. And over his head hovered worries as a vulture hovers over a carcass, until he reached a beautiful lake surrounded by magnificent marble statuary.

He sat there pondering the water which poured from the mouths of the statues like thoughts flowing freely from a lover's imagination, and contemplating heavily his palace which stood upon a knoll like a birth-mark upon the cheek of a maiden. His fancy revealed to him the pages of his life's drama which he read with falling tears that veiled his eyes and prevented him from viewing man's feeble additions to Nature.

He looked back with piercing regret to the images of his early life, woven into pattern by the gods, until he could no longer control his anguish. He said aloud, "Yesterday I was grazing my sheep in the green valley, enjoying my existence, sounding my flute, and holding my head high. Today I am a prisoner of greed. Gold leads into gold, then into restlessness, and finally into crushing misery.

"Yesterday I was like a singing bird, soaring freely here and there in the fields. Today I am a slave to fickle wealth, society's rules, the city's customs, and purchased friends, pleasing the people by conforming to the strange and narrow laws of man. I was born to be free and enjoy the bounty of life, but I find myself like a beast of burden so heavily laden with gold that his back is breaking.

"Where are the spacious plains, the singing brooks, the pure breeze, the closeness of Nature? Where is my deity? I have lost all! Naught remains save loneliness that saddens me, gold that ridicules me, slaves who curse to my back, and a palace that I have erected as a tomb for my happiness, and in whose greatness I have lost my heart.

"Yesterday I roamed the prairies and the hills together with the Bedouin's daughter; Virtue was our companion, Love our delight, and the moon our guardian. Today I am among women with shallow beauty who sell themselves for gold and diamonds.

"Yesterday I was carefree, sharing with the shepherds all the joy of life; eating, playing, working, singing, and dancing together to the music of the heart's truth. Today I find myself among the people like a frightened lamb among the wolves. As I walk in the roads, they gaze at me with hateful eyes and point at me with scorn and jealousy, and as I steal through the park I see frowning faces all about me.

"Yesterday I was rich in happiness and today I am poor in gold.

"Yesterday I was a happy shepherd looking upon my herd as a merciful king looks with pleasure upon his contented subjects. Today I am a slave standing before my wealth, my wealth which robbed me of the beauty of life I once knew.

"Forgive me, my Judge! I did not know that riches would put my life in fragments and lead me into the dungeons of harshness and stupidity. What I thought was glory is naught but an eternal inferno."

He gathered himself wearily and walked slowly toward the palace, sighing and repeating, "Is this what people call wealth? Is this the god I am serving and worshipping? Is this what I seek of the earth? Why can I not trade it for one particle of contentment? Who would sell me one beautiful thought for a ton of gold? Who would give me one moment of love for a handful of gems? Who would grant me an eye that can see others' hearts, and take all my coffers in barter?"

As he reached the palace gates he turned and looked toward the city as Jeremiah gazed toward Jerusalem. He raised his arms in woeful lament and shouted, "Oh people of the noisome city, who are living in darkness, hastening toward misery, preaching falsehood, and speaking with stupidity ... until when shall you remain ignorant? Until when shall you abide in the filth of life and continue to desert its gardens? Why wear you tattered robes of narrowness while the silk raiment of Nature's beauty is fashioned for you? The lamp of wisdom is dimming; it is time to furnish it with oil. The house of true fortune is being destroyed; it is time to rebuild it and guard it. The thieves of ignorance have stolen the treasure of your peace; it is time to retake it!"

At that moment a poor man stood before him and stretched forth his hand for alms. As he looked at the beggar, his lips parted, his eyes brightened with a softness, and his face radiated kindness. It was as if the yesterday he had lamented by the lake had come to greet him. He embraced the pauper with affection and filled his hand with gold, and with a voice sincere with the sweetness of love he said, "Come back tomorrow and bring with you your fellow sufferers. All your possessions will be restored."

He entered his palace saying, "Everything in life is good; even gold, for it teaches a lesson. Money is like a stringed instrument; he who does not know how to use it properly will hear only discordant music. Money is like love; it kills slowly and painfully the one who withholds it, and it enlivens the other who turns it upon his fellow men."

THE MERMAIDS

In the depths of the sea, surrounding the nearby islands where the sun rises, there is a profoundness. And there, where the pearl exists in abundance, lay a corpse of a youth encircled by sea maidens of long golden hair; they stared upon him with their deep blue eyes, conversing among themselves with musical voices. And the conversation, heard by the depths and conveyed to the shore by the waves, was brought to me by the frolicsome breeze.

One of them said, "This is a human who entered into our world yesterday, while our sea was raging."

And the second one said, "The sea was not raging. Man, who claims that he is a descendant of the Gods, was making iron war, and his blood is being shed until the colour of the water is now crimson; this human is a victim of war."

The third one ventured, "I do not know what war is, but I do know that man, after having subdued the land, became aggressive and resolved to subdue the sea. He devised a strange object which carried him upon the seas, whereupon our severe Neptune became enraged over his greed. In order to please Neptune, man commenced offering gifts and sacrifices, and the still body before us is the most recent gift of man to our great and terrible Neptune."

The fourth one asserted, "How great is Neptune, and how cruel is his heart! If I were the Sultan of the sea I would refuse to accept such payment... Come now, and let us examine this ransom. Perhaps we may enlighten ourselves as to the human clan."

The mermaids approached the youth, probed the

pockets, and found a message close to his heart; one of them read it aloud to the others:

"My Beloved:

"Midnight has again come, and I have no consolation except my pouring tears, and naught to comfort me save my hope in your return to me from between the bloody paws of war. I cannot forget your words when you took departure: 'Every man has a trust of tears which must be returned some day.'

"I know not what to say, My Beloved, but my soul will pour itself into parchment... my soul that suffers through separation, but is consoled by Love that renders pain a joy, and sorrow a happiness. When Love unified our hearts, and we looked to the day when our two hearts would be joined by the mighty breath of God, War shouted her horrible call and you followed her, prompted by your duty to the leaders.

"What is this duty that separates the lovers, and causes the women to become widows, and the children to become orphans? What is this patriotism which provokes wars and destroys kingdoms through trifles? And what cause can be more than trifling when compared to but one life? What is this duty which invites poor villagers, who are looked upon as nothing by the strong and by the sons of the inherited nobility, to die for the glory of their oppressors? If duty destroys peace among nations, and patriotism disturbs the tranquillity of man's life, then let us say, 'Peace be with duty and patriotism.'

"No, no, My Beloved! Heed not my words! Be

courageous and faithful to your country... Hearken not unto the talk of a damsel, blinded by Love, and lost through farewell and aloneness... If Love will not restore you to me in this life, then Love will surely join us in the coming life.

Your Forever"

The mermaids replaced the note under the youth's raiment and swam silently and sorrowfully away. As they gathered together at a distance from the body of the dead soldier, one of them said, "The human heart is more severe than the cruel heart of Neptune."

SECRETS OF THE HEART

A majestic mansion stood under the wings of the silent night, as Life stands under the cover of Death. In it sat a maiden at an ivory desk, leaning her beautiful head on her soft hand, as a withering lily leans upon its petals. She looked around, feeling like a miserable prisoner, struggling to penetrate the walls of the dungeon with her eyes in order to witness Life walking in the procession of Freedom.

The hours passed like the ghosts of the night, as a procession chanting the dirge of her sorrow, and the maiden felt secure with the shedding of her tears in anguished solitude. When she could not resist the pressure of her suffering any longer, and as she felt that she was in full possession of the treasured secrets of her heart, she took the quill and commenced mingling her tears with ink upon parchment, and she inscribed:

"My Beloved Sister,

"When the heart becomes congested with secrets, and the eyes begin to burn from the searing tears, and the ribs are about to burst with the growing of the heart's confinement, one cannot find expression for such a labyrinth except by a surge of release.

"Sorrowful persons find joy in lamentation, and lovers encounter comfort and condolence in dreams, and the oppressed delight in receiving sympathy. I am writing to you now because I feel like a poet who fancies the beauty of objects whose impression he composes in verse while being ruled by a divine power... I am like a child of the starving poor who cries for food, instigated by bitterness of hunger, disregarding the plight of his poor and merciful mother and her defeat in life.

"Listen to my painful story, my dear sister, and weep with me, for sobbing is like a prayer, and the tears of mercy are like a charity because they come forth from a living and sensitive and good soul and they are not shed in vain. It was the will of my father when I married a noble and rich man. My father was like most of the rich, whose only joy in life is to improve their wealth by adding more gold to coffers in fear of poverty, and curry nobility with grandeur in anticipation of the attacks of the black days... I find myself now, with all my love and dreams, a victim upon a golden alter which I hate, and an inherited honour which I despise.

"I respect my husband because he is generous and kind to all; he endeavours to bring happiness to me, and spends his gold to please my heart, but I have found that the impression of all these things is not worth one moment of a true and divine love. Do not ridicule me, my sister, for I am now a most enlightened person regarding the needs of a woman's heart—that throbbing heart which is like a bird flying in the spacious sky of love.... It is like a vase replenished with the wine of the ages that has been pressed for the sipping souls.... It is like a book in whose pages one reads the chapters of happiness and misery, joy and pain, laughter and sorrow. No one can read this book except the true companion who is the other half of the woman, created for her since the beginning of the world.

"Yes, I became most knowing amongst all women as to the purpose of the soul and meaning of the heart, for I have found that my magnificent horses and beautiful carriages and glittering coffers of gold and sublime nobility are not worth one glance from the eyes of that poor young man who is patiently waiting and suffering the pangs of bitterness and misery.... That youth who is oppressed by the cruelty and will of my father, and imprisoned in the narrow and melancholy jail of Life...

"Please, my dear, do not contrive to console me, for the calamity through which I have realised the power of my love is my great consoler. Now I am looking forward from behind my tears and awaiting the coming of Death to lead me to where I will meet the companion of my soul and embrace him as I did before we entered this strange world.

"Do not think evil of me, for I am doing my duty as a faithful wife, and complying calmly and patiently with the laws and rules of man. I honour my husband with my sense, and respect him with my heart, and revere him with my soul, but there is a withholding, for God gave part of me to my beloved before I knew him.

"Heaven willed that I spend my life with a man not meant for me, and I am wasting my days silently according to the will of Heaven; but if the gates of Eternity do not open, I will remain with the beautiful half of my soul and look back to the Past, and that Past is this Present... I shall look at life as Spring looks at Winter, and contemplate the obstacles of Life as one who has climbed the rough trail and reached the mountain top."

At that moment the maiden ceased writing and hid her face with her cupped hands and wept bitterly. Her heart declined to entrust to the pen its most sacred secrets, but restored to the pouring of dry tears that dispersed quickly and mingled with the gentle ether, the haven of the lovers' souls and the flowers' spirits. After a moment she took the quill and added, "Do you remember that youth? Do you recollect the rays which emanated from his eyes, and the sorrowful signs upon his face? Do you recall that laughter which bespoke the tears of a mother, torn from her only child? Can you retrace his serene voice speaking the echo of a distant valley? Do you remember him meditating and staring longingly and calmly at objects and speaking of them in strange words, and then bending his head and sighing as if fearing to reveal the secrets of his great heart? Do you recall his dreams and beliefs? Do you recollect all these things in a youth whom humanity counts as one of her children and upon whom my father looked with eyes of superiority because he is higher than earthly greed and nobler than inherited grandeur?

"You know, my dear sister, that I am a martyr in this belittling world, and a victim of ignorance. Will you sympathise with a sister who sits in the silence of the horrible night pouring down the contents of her inner self and revealing to you her heart's secrets? I am sure that you will sympathise with me, for I know that Love has visited your heart."

Dawn came, and the maiden surrendered herself to Slumber, hoping to find sweeter and more gentle dreams than those she had encountered in her awakeness...

NATURE AND MAN

At daybreak I sat in a field, holding converse with Nature, while Man rested peacefully under coverlets of slumber. I lay in the green grass and meditated upon these questions: "Is Truth Beauty? Is Beauty Truth?"

And in my thoughts I found myself carried far from mankind, and my imagination lifted the veil of matter that hid my inner self. My soul expanded and I was brought closer to Nature and her secrets, and my ears were opened to the language of her wonders.

As I sat thus deep in thought, I felt a breeze passing through the branches of the trees, and I heard a sighing like that of a strayed orphan.

"Why do you sigh, gentle breeze?" I asked.

And the breeze replied, "Because I have come from the city that is aglow with the heat of the sun, and the seeds of plagues and contaminations cling to my pure garments. Can you blame me for grieving?"

Then I looked at the tear-stained faces of the flowers, and heard their soft lament. And I asked, "Why do you weep, my lovely flowers?"

One of the flowers raised her gentle head and whispered, "We weep because Man will come and cut us down, and offer us for sale in the markets of the city."

And another flower added, "In the evening, when we are wilted, he will throw us on the refuse heap. We weep because the cruel hand of Man snatches us from our native haunts."

And I heard the brook lamenting like a widow mourning

her dead child and I asked, "Why do you weep, my pure brook?"

And the brook replied, "Because I am compelled to go to the city where Man contemns me and spurns me for stronger drinks and makes of me a scavenger for his offal, pollutes my purity, and turns my goodness to filth."

And I heard the birds grieving, and I asked, "Why do you cry, my beautiful birds?" And one of them flew near, and perched at the tip of a branch and said, "The sons of Adam will soon come into this field with their deadly weapons and make war upon us as if we were their mortal enemies. We are now taking leave of one another, for we know not which of us will escape the wrath of Man. Death follows us wherever we go."

Now the sun rose from behind the mountain peaks, and gilded the treetops with coronals. I looked upon this beauty and asked myself, "Why must Man destroy what Nature has built?"

YOUTH AND HOPE

Youth walked before me and I followed him until we came to a distant field. There he stopped, and gazed at the clouds that drifted over the horizon like a flock of white lambs. Then he looked at the trees whose naked branches pointed toward the sky as if praying to Heaven for the return of their foliage.

And I said, "Where are we now, Youth?"

And he replied, "We are in the field of Bewilderment. Take heed."

And I said, "let us go back at once, for this desolate place affrights me, and the sight of the clouds and the naked trees saddens my heart.'

And he replied, "Be patient. Perplexity is the beginning of knowledge."

Then I looked around me and saw a form moving gracefully toward us and I asked, "Who is this woman?"

And Youth replied, "This is Melpomene, daughter of Zeus, and Muse of Tragedy."

"Oh, happy Youth!" I exclaimed, "what does Tragedy want of me, while you are at my side?"

And he answered, "She has come to show you the earth and its sorrows; for he who has not looked on Sorrow will never see Joy."

Then the spirit laid a hand upon my eyes. When she withdrew it, Youth was gone, and I was alone, divested of my earthly garments, and I cried, "Daughter of Zeus, where is Youth?"

Melpomene did not answer; but took me up under her wings, and carried me to the summit of a high mountain. Below me I saw the earth and all in it, spread out like the pages of a book, upon which were inscribed the secrets of the universe. I stood in awe beside the maiden, pondered the mystery of Man, and struggled to decipher Life's symbols.

And I saw woeful things: The Angels of Happiness warring with the Devils of Misery, and standing between them was Man, now drawn one way by Hope and now another by Despair.

I saw Love and Hate dallying with the human heart; Love concealing Man's guilt and besotting him with the wine of submission, praise and flattery; while Hatred provoked him, and sealed his ears and blinded his eyes to Truth.

And I beheld the city crouching like a child of its slums and snatching at the garment of the son of Adam. From afar I saw the lovely fields weeping over man's sorrow. I beheld priests foaming like sly foxes; and false messiahs contriving and conspiring against Man's happiness.

And I saw Man calling upon Wisdom for deliverance; but Wisdom did not hearken to his cries, for he had contemned her when she spoke to him in the streets of the city.

And I saw preachers gazing in adoration toward the heavens, while their hearts were interred in the pits of Greed.

I saw a youth winning a maiden's heart with sweet speech; but their true feelings were asleep, and their divinity was far away.

I saw the lawmakers chattering idly, selling their wares in

the market places of Deceit and Hypocrisy.

I saw physicians toying with the souls of the simple hearted and trustful. I saw the ignorant sitting with the wise, exalting their past to the throne of glory, adorning their present with the robes of plenty, and preparing a couch of luxury for the future.

I saw the wretched poor sowing the seed, and the strong reaping; and oppression, miscalled Law, standing guard.

I saw the thieves of Ignorance despoiling the treasures of Knowledge, while the sentinels of Light lay drowned in the deep sleep of inaction.

And I saw two lovers; but the woman was like a lute in the hand of a man who cannot play, but understands only harsh sounds.

And I beheld the forces of Knowledge laying siege to the city of Inherited Privilege; but they were few in number and were soon dispersed.

And I saw Freedom walking alone, knocking at doors, and asking for shelter, but no one heeded her pleas. Then I saw Prodigality striding in splendour, and the multitude acclaiming her as Liberty.

I saw Religion buried in books, and Doubt stood in her place.

And I saw Man wearing the garments of Patience as a cloak for Cowardice and calling Sloth Tolerance, and Fear Courtesy.

I saw the intruder sitting at the board of Knowledge, uttering folly, but the guests were silent.

I saw gold in the hands of the wasteful, a means of evil-doing; and in the hands of the miserly as a bait for hatred.

But in the hands of the wise I saw no gold.

When I beheld all these things, I cried out in pain, "Oh Daughter of Zeus, is this indeed the Earth? Is this Man?"

In a soft and anguished voice she replied, "What you see is the Soul's path, and it is paved with sharp stones and carpeted with thorns. This is only the shadow of Man. This is Night. But wait! Morning will soon be here!"

Then she laid a gentle hand upon my eyes, and when she withdrew it, behold! There was Youth walking slowly by my side, and ahead of us, leading the way, marched Hope.

MY SOUL PREACHED TO ME

My soul preached to me and taught me to love that which the people abhor and befriend him whom they revile.

My soul showed me that Love prides itself not only in the one who loves, but also in the beloved.

Ere my soul preached to me, Love was in my heart as a tiny thread fastened between two pegs.

But now Love has become a halo whose beginning is its end, and whose end is its beginning. It surrounds every being and extends slowly to embrace all that shall be.

My soul advised me and taught me to perceive the hidden beauty of the skin, figure, and hue. She instructed me to meditate upon that which the people call ugly until its true charm and delight appear.

Ere my soul counselled me, I saw Beauty like a trembling torch between columns of smoke. Now since the smoke has vanished, I see naught save the flame.

My soul preached to me and taught me to listen to the voices which the tongue and the larynx and the lips do not utter.

Ere my soul preached to me, I heard naught but clamour and wailing. But now I eagerly attend Silence and hear its choirs singing the hymns of the ages and the songs of the firmament announcing the secrets of the Unseen.

My soul preached to me and instructed me to drink the

wine that cannot be pressed and cannot be poured from cups that hands can lift or lips can touch.

Ere my soul preached to me, my thirst was like a dim spark hidden under the ashes that can be extinguished by a swallow of water.

But now my longing has become my cup, my affections my wine, and my loneliness my intoxication; yet, in this unquenchable thirst there is eternal joy.

My soul preached to me and taught me to touch that which has not become incarnate; my soul revealed to me that whatever we touch is part of our desire.

But now my fingers have turned into mist penetrating that which is seen in the universe and mingling with the Unseen.

My soul instructed me to inhale the scent that no myrtle or incense emits. Ere my soul preached to me, I craved the scent of perfume in the gardens or in flasks or in censers.

But now I can savour the incense that is not burnt for offering or sacrifice. And I fill my heart with a fragrance that has never been wafted by the frolicsome breeze of space.

My soul preached to me and taught me to say, "I am ready" when the Unknown and Danger call on me.

Ere my soul preached to me, I answered no voice save the voice of the crier whom I knew, and walked not save upon the easy and smooth path.

Now the Unknown has become a steed that I can mount in order to reach the Unknown; and the plain has turned into a ladder on whose steps I climb to the summit.

My soul spoke to me and said, "Do not measure Time by saying, 'There was yesterday, and there shall be tomorrow.'"

And ere my soul spoke to me, I imagined the Past as an

epoch that never returned, and the Future as one that could never be reached.

Now I realise that the present moment contains all time and within it is all that can be hoped for, done and realised.

My soul preached to me exhorting me not to limit space by saying, "Here, there, and yonder."

Ere my soul preached to me, I felt that wherever I walked was far from any other space.

Now I realise that wherever I am contains all places; and the distance that I walk embraces all distances.

My soul instructed me and advised me to stay awake while others sleep. And to surrender to slumber when others are astir.

Ere my soul preached to me, I saw not their dreams in my sleep, neither did they observe my vision.

Now I never sail the vessel of my dreams unless they watch me, and they never soar into the sky of their vision unless I rejoice in their freedom.

My soul preached to me and said, "Do not be delighted because of praise, and do not be distressed because of blame."

Ere my soul counselled me, I doubted the worth of my work.

Now I realise that the trees blossom in Spring and bear fruit in Summer without seeking praise; and they drop their leaves in Autumn and become naked in Winter without fearing blame.

My soul preached to me and showed me that I am neither more than the pygmy, nor less than the giant.

Ere my soul preached to me, I looked upon humanity as two men: one weak, whom I pitied, and the other strong, whom I followed or resisted in defiance.

But now I have learned that I was as both are and made from the same elements. My origin is their origin, my conscience is their conscience, my contention is their contention, and my pilgrimage is their pilgrimage.

If they sin, I am also a sinner. If they do well, I take pride in their well-doing. If they rise, I rise with them. If they stay inert, I share their slothfulness.

My soul spoke to me and said, "The lantern which you carry is not yours, and the song that you sing was not composed within your heart, for even if you bear the light, you are not the light, and even if you are a lute fastened with strings, you are not the lute player."

My soul preached to me, my brother, and taught me much. And your soul has preached and taught as much to you. For you and I are one, and there is no variance between us save that I urgently declare that which is in my inner self, while you keep as a secret that which is within you. But in your secrecy there is a sort of virtue.

SEVEN REPRIMANDS

I reprimanded my soul seven times!

The first time: when I attempted to exalt myself by exploiting the weak.

The second time: when I feigned a limp before those who were crippled.

The third time: when, given a choice, I elected the easy rather than difficult.

The fourth time: when I made a mistake I consoled myself with the mistakes of others.

The fifth time: when I was docile because of fear and then claimed to be strong in patience.

The sixth time: when I held my garments upraised to avoid the mud of Life.

The seventh time: when I stood in hymnal to God and considered the singing a virtue.

VISION

When Night came and Slumber spread its garment upon the face of the earth, I left my bed and walked toward the sea saying, "The sea never sleeps, and in its vigil there is consolation for a sleepless soul."

When I reached the shore, the mist from the mountains had engauzed the region as a veil adorns the face of a young woman. I gazed at the teeming waves and listened to their praise of God and meditated upon the eternal power hidden within them—that power which runs with the tempest and rises with the volcano and smiles through the lips of the roses and sings with the brooks.

Then I saw three phantoms sitting upon a rock. I stumbled toward them as if some power were pulling me against my will.

Within a few paces from the phantoms, I halted as though held still by a magic force. At that moment one of the phantoms stood up and in a voice that seemed to rise from the depth of the sea said:

"Life without Love is like a tree without blossom and fruit. And Love without Beauty is like flowers without scent and fruits without seeds.... Life, Love, and Beauty are three persons in one, who cannot be separated or changed."

A second phantom spoke with a voice that roared like cascading water and said:

"Life without Rebellion is like seasons without Spring. And Rebellion without Right is like Spring in an arid desert.... Life, Rebellion, and Right are three-in-one who cannot be changed or separated."

Then the third phantom in a voice like a clap of thunder spoke:

"Life without Freedom is like a body without a soul, and Freedom without Thought is like a confused spirit... Life, Freedom, and Thought are three-in-one, and are everlasting and never pass away."

Then the three phantoms stood up together, and with one tremendous voice said:

"That which Love begets,
That which Rebellion creates,
That which Freedom rears,
Are three manifestations of God.
And God is the expression
Of the intelligent Universe."

At that moment Silence mingled with the rustling of invisible wings and trembling of ethereal bodies; and it prevailed.

I closed my eyes and listened to the echoes of the sayings which I had just heard, and when I opened them I saw nothing but the sea wreathed in mist. I walked toward the rock where the three phantoms were sitting, but I saw naught save a column of incense spiralling toward heaven.

O SOUL

O Soul, if I did not covet immortality, I would never have learned the song which has been sung through all of time.

Rather, I would have been a suicide, nothing remaining of me except my ashes hidden within the tomb.

O soul! If I had not been baptised with tears and my eyes had not been mascaraed by ghosts of sickness, I would not have seen life as through a veil, darkly.

O soul! Life is a darkness which ends as in the sunburst of day.

The yearning of my heart tells me there is peace in the grave.

O soul! If some fool tells you the soul perishes like the body and that which dies never returns, tell him the flower perishes but the seed remains and lies before us as the secret of life everlasting.

HANDFUL OF BEACH SAND

When you tell your trouble to your neighbour you present him with a part of your heart. If he possesses a great soul, he thanks you; if he possesses a small one, he belittles you.

Progress is not merely improving the past; it is moving forward toward the future.

A hungry savage picks fruit from a tree and eats it; a hungry civilised man buys it from a man who, in turn, buys it from the man who picks it.

Art is one step from the visibly known toward the unknown.

The earth breathes, we live; it pauses in breath, we die.

Man's eye is a magnifier; it shows him the earth much larger than it is.

I abstain from the people who consider insolence, bravery and tenderness cowardice. And I abstain from those who consider chatter wisdom and silence ignorance.

They tell me: If you see a slave sleeping, do not wake him lest he be dreaming of freedom.

I tell them: If you see a slave sleeping, wake him and explain to him freedom.

Contradiction is a lower degree of intelligence.

Bravery is a volcano; the seed of wavering does not grow on its crater.

The river continues on its way to the sea, broken the wheel of the mill or not.

The greater your joy or your sorrow, the smaller the world in your eyes.

Learning nourishes the seed but it gives you no seed of its own.

I use hate as a weapon to defend myself; had I been strong, I would never have needed that kind of weapon.

There are among the people murderers who have never committed murder, thieves who have never stolen and liars who have spoken nothing but the truth.

Keep me away from the wisdom which does not cry, the philosophy which does not laugh and the greatness which does not bow before children.

O great intelligent Being! hidden and existing in and for the universe, You can hear me because You are within me and You can see me because You are all-seeing; please drop within my soul a seed of Your wisdom to grow a sapling in Your forest and to give of Your fruit.

Amen!

SOLITUDE AND SECLUSION

Life is an island in an ocean of solitude and seclusion.

Life is an island, rocks are its desires, trees its dreams, and flowers its loneliness, and it is in the middle of an ocean of solitude and seclusion.

Your life, my friend, is an island separated from all other islands and continents. Regardless of how many boats you send to other shores or how many ships arrive upon your shores, you yourself are an island separated by its own pains, secluded in its happiness and far away in its compassion and hidden in its secrets and mysteries.

I saw you, my friend, sitting upon a mound of gold, happy in your wealth and great in your riches and believing that a handful of gold is the secret chain that links the thoughts of the people with your own thoughts and links their feeling with your own.

I saw you as a great conqueror leading a conquering army toward the fortress, then destroying and capturing it.

On second glance I found beyond the wall of your treasures a heart trembling in its solitude and seclusion like the trembling of a thirsty man within a cage of gold and jewels, but without water.

I saw you, my friend, sitting on a throne of glory, surrounded by people extolling your charity, enumerating your gifts, gazing upon you as if they were in the presence of a prophet lifting their souls up into the planets and stars. I saw you looking at them, contentment and strength upon your face, as if you were to them as the soul is to the body.

On the second look I saw your secluded self standing

beside your throne, suffering in its seclusion and quaking in its loneliness. I saw that self stretching its hands as if begging from unseen ghosts. I saw it looking above the shoulders of the people to a far horizon, empty of everything except its solitude and seclusion.

I saw you, my friend, passionately in love with a beautiful woman, filling her palms with you kisses as she looked at you with sympathy and affection in her eyes and the sweetness of motherhood on her lips; I said, secretly, that love has erased his solitude and removed his seclusion and he is now within the eternal soul which draws toward itself, with love, those who were separated by solitude and seclusion.

On the second look I saw behind your soul another lonely soul, like a fog, trying in vain to become a drop of tears in the palm of that woman.

Your life, my friend, is a residence far away from any other residence and neighbours.

Your inner soul is a home far away from other homes named after you. If this residence is dark, you cannot light it with your neighbour's lamp; if it is empty you cannot fill it with the riches of your neighbour; were it in the middle of a desert, you could not move it to a garden planted by someone else.

Your inner soul, my friend, is surrounded with solitude and seclusion. Were it not for this solitude and this seclusion you would not be you and I would not be I. If it were not for that solitude and seclusion, I would, if I heard your voice, think myself to be speaking; yet, if I saw your face, I would imagine that I were looking into a mirror.

THE SONS OF THE GODDESS AND THE SONS OF THE MONKEYS

How strange Time is, and how queer we are! Time has really changed, and lo, it has changed us too. It walked one step forward, unveiled its face, alarmed us and then elated us.

Yesterday we complained about Time and trembled at its terrors. But today we have learned to love it and revere it, for we now understand its intents, its natural disposition, its secrets, and its mysteries.

Yesterday we crawled in fright like shuddering ghosts between the fears of the night and the menaces of the day. But today we walk joyously towards the mountain peak, the dwelling place of the raging tempest and the birthplace of thunder.

Yesterday we ate our bread kneaded with blood, and we drank our water mixed with tears. But today we began to receive the manna from the hands of the morning brides and drank the aged wine scented with the sweet breath of Spring.

Yesterday we were a toy in the hands of Destiny. But today Destiny has awakened from her intoxication to play and laugh and walk with us. We do not follow her but she follows us.

Yesterday we burned incense before the idols and offered sacrifices to the angry gods. But today we burn incense and offer sacrifices to our own being, for the greatest and most beautiful of all gods has raised his temple in our hearts.

Yesterday we bowed to the kings and bent our necks to

the sultans. But today we do not pay reverence save to Right and we follow no one except Beauty and Love.

Yesterday we honoured false prophets and sorcerers. But today Time has changed, and lo, it has changed us too. We can now stare at the face of the sun and listen to the songs of the sea, and nothing can shake us except a cyclone.

Yesterday we tore down the temples of our souls and from their debris we built tombs for our forefathers. But today our souls have turned into sacred alters that the ghosts of the Past cannot approach, that the fleshless fingers of the dead cannot touch.

We were a silent thought hidden in the corners of Oblivion. Today we are a strong voice that can make the firmament reverberate.

We were a tiny spark buried under the ashes. Today we are a raging fire burning at the head of the valley.

We spent many a night awake, with the earth as our pillow and the snow as our blanket.

Like sheep without a shepherd we flocked together many nights grazing on our thoughts, and chewing the cud of our emotions; yet we remained hungry and athirst.

Oftentime we stood between a passing day and a coming night lamenting our withering youth and longing for someone unknown, and gazing at the void and dark sky listening to the moaning of Silence and the shrieking of nothingness.

Those ages passed like wolves among the graves. But today the skies are clear, and we can rest peacefully upon divine beds and welcome our thoughts and dreams, and embrace our desires. Grasping with untrembling fingers the torches that sway around us, we can talk to the genii with explicit meaning. As the choirs of angels pass us, they become intoxicated with the longing of our hearts and the hymns of our souls.

Yesterday we were, and today we are! This is the will of the goddess among the sons of the goddess. What is your will, oh sons of the monkeys? Have you walked a single step forward since you came forth from the crevices of the earth? Have you gazed toward heaven since Satan opened your eyes? Have you uttered a word from the book of Right since the lips of vipers kissed your lips? Or have you listened a moment to the song of Life since Death closed your ears?

Seventy thousand years ago I passed by and saw you moving like insects inside the caves; and seven minutes ago I glanced at you through the crystal glass of my window and saw you walking through the alleys fettered by slavery while the wings of Death hovered over you. You look the same today as you looked yesterday; and tomorrow, and the day after it, you shall look as I saw you in the beginning.

Yesterday we were, and today we are! This is the will of the goddess among the sons of the goddess; what is your will, oh sons of the monkeys?

THE TWO HUNTERS

Upon a day in May, Joy and Sorrow met beside a lake. They greeted one another, and they sat down near the quiet waters and conversed.

Joy spoke of the beauty which is upon the earth, and of the daily wonder of life in the forest and among the hills, and of the songs heard at dawn and eventide.

And Sorrow spoke, and agreed with all that Joy had said; for Sorrow knew the magic of the hour and the beauty thereof. And Sorrow was eloquent when he spoke of May in the fields and among the hills.

And Joy and Sorrow talked long together, and they agreed upon all things of which they knew.

Now there passed by on the other side of the lake two hunters. And as they looked across the water on of them said, "I wonder who are those two persons?" And the other said, "Did you say two? I see only one."

The first hunter said, "But there are two." And the second said, "There is only one that I can see, and the reflection in the lake is only one."

"Nay, there are two," said the first hunter, "and the reflection in the still water is of two persons."

But the second man said again, "Only one do I see." And again the other said, "But I see two so plainly."

And even to this day one hunter says that the other sees double; while the other says, "My friend is somewhat blind."

THE QUEST

A thousand years ago two philosophers met on a slope of Lebanon, and one said to the other, "Where goest thou?"

And the other answered, "I am seeking after the fountain of youth which I know wells out among these hills. I have found writings which tell of that fountain flowering towards the sun. And you, what are you seeking?"

The first man answered, "I am seeking after the mystery of death."

Then each of the two philosophers conceived that the other was lacking in his great science, and they began to wrangle, and to accuse each other of spiritual blindness.

Now while the two philosophers were loud upon the wind, a stranger, a man who was deemed a simpleton in his own village, passed by, and when he heard the two in hot dispute, he stood awhile and listened to their argument.

Then he came near to them and said, "My good men, it seems that you both really belong to the same school of philosophy, and that you are speaking of the same thing, only you speak in different words. One of you seeks the fountain of youth, and the other seeks the mystery of death. Yet indeed they are but one, and as one they dwell in you both."

Then the stranger turned away saying, "Farewell, sages." And as he departed he laughed a patient laughter.

The two philosophers looked at each other in silence for a moment, and then they laughed also. And one of them said, "Well now, shall we not walk and seek together?"

LOVE AND HATE

A woman said unto a man, "I love you."

And the man said, "It is in my heart to be worthy of your love."

And the woman said, "You love me not?" And the man only gazed upon her and said nothing.

Then the woman cried aloud, "I hate you." And the man said "Then it is also in my heart to be worthy of your hate."

THE MADMAN

It was in the garden of a madhouse that I met a youth with a face pale and lovely and full of wonder.

And I sat beside him upon the bench, and I said, "Why are you here?"

And he looked at me in astonishment, and he said, "It is an unseemly question, yet I will answer you. My father would make of me a reproduction of himself; so also would my uncle. My mother would have me the image of her illustrious father. My sister would hold up her seafaring husband as the perfect example for me to follow. My brother thinks I should be like him, a fine athlete.

"And my teachers also, the doctor of philosophy, and the music-master, and the logician, they too were determined, and each would have me but a reflection of his own face in a mirror.

"Therefore I came to this place. I find it more sane here. At least, I can be myself."

Then of a sudden he turned to me and he said, "But tell me, were you also driven to this place by education and good counsel?"

And I answered, "No, I am a visitor."

And he said, "Oh, you are one of those who live in the madhouse on the other side of the wall."

THE STATUE

Once there lived a man among the hills who possessed a statue wrought by an ancient master. It lay at his door face downward and he was not mindful of it.

One day there passed by his house a man from the city, a man of knowledge, and seeing the statue he inquired of the owner if he would sell it.

The owner laughed and said, "And pray who would want to buy that dull and dirty stone?"

The man from the city said, "I will give you this piece of silver for it."

And the other man was astonished and delighted.

The statue was removed to the city, upon the back of an elephant. And after many moons the man from the hills visited the city, and as he walked the streets he saw a crowd before a shop, and a man with a loud voice was crying, "Come ye in and behold the most beautiful, the most wonderful statue in all the world. Only two silver pieces to look upon this most marvelous work of a master."

Thereupon the man from the hills paid two silver pieces and entered the shop to see the statue that he himself had sold for one piece of silver.

THE TWO GUARDIAN ANGELS

On an evening two angels met at the city gate, and they greeted one another, and they conversed.

The one angel said, "What are you doing these days, and what work is given you?"

And the other answered, "It has been assigned me to be the guardian of a fallen man who lives down in the valley, a great sinner, most degraded. Let me assure you it is an important task, and I work hard."

The first angel said, "That is an easy commission. I have often known sinners, and have been their guardian many a time. But it has now been assigned me to be the guardian of the good saint who lives in a bower out yonder. And I assure you that is an exceedingly difficult work, and most subtle."

Said the first angel, "This is but assumption. How can guarding a saint be harder than guarding a sinner?"

And the other answered, "What impertinence, to call me assumptious! I have stated but the truth. Methinks it is you who are assumptious!"

Then the angels wrangled and fought, first with words and then with fists and wings.

While they were fighting an archangel came by. And he stopped them, and said, "Why do you fight? And what is it all about? Know you not that it is most unbecoming for guardian angels to fight at the city gate? Tell me, what is your disagreement?"

Then both angels spoke at once, each claiming that the work given him was the harder, and that he deserved the greater recognition.

The archangel shook his head and bethought him.

Then he said, "My friends, I cannot say now which one of you has the greater claim upon honour and reward. But since the power is bestowed in me, therefore for peace' sake and for good guardianship, I give to each of you the other's occupation, since each of you insists that the other's task is the easier one. Now go hence and be happy at your work."

The angels thus ordered went their ways. But each one looked backward with greater anger at the archangel. And in his heart each was saying, "Oh, these archangels! Every day they make life harder and still harder for us angels!"

But the archangel stood there, and once more he bethought him. And he said in his heart, "We have indeed, to be watchful and to keep guard over our guardian angels."

THE TWO LEARNED MEN

Once there lived in the ancient city of Afkar two learned men who hated and belittled each other's learning. For one of them denied the existence of the gods and the other was a believer.

One day the two met in the market-place, and amidst their followers they began to dispute and to argue about the existence or the non-existence of the gods. And after hours of contention they parted.

That evening the unbeliever went to the temple and prostrated himself before the alter and prayed the gods to forgive his wayward past.

And the same hour the other learned man, he who had upheld the gods, burned his sacred books. For he had become an unbeliever.

THE GOOD GOD AND THE EVIL GOD

The Good God and the Evil God met on the mountain top.

The Good God said, "Good day to you, brother."

The Evil God made no answer.

And the Good God said, "You are in a bad humour today."

"Yes," said the Evil God, "for of late I have been often mistaken for you, called by your name, and treated as if I were you, and it ill-pleases me."

And the Good God said, "But I too have been mistaken for you and called by your name."

The Evil God walked away cursing the stupidity of man.

THE LOVE SONG

A poet once wrote a love song and it was beautiful. And he made many copies of it, and sent them to his friends and his acquaintances, both men and women, and even to a young woman whom he had met but once, who lived beyond the mountains.

And in a day or two a messenger came from the young woman bringing a letter. And in the letter she said, "Let me assure you, I am deeply touched by the love song that you have written to me. Come now, and see my father and my mother, and we shall make arrangements for the betrothal."

And the poet answered the letter, and he said to her, "My friend, it was but a song of love out of a poet's heart, sung by every man to every woman."

And she wrote again to him saying, "Hypocrite and liar in words! From this day unto my coffin-day I shall hate all poets for your sake."

THE THREE GIFTS

Once in the city of Becharre there lived a gracious prince who was loved and honoured by all his subjects.

But there was one exceedingly poor man who was bitter against the prince, and who wagged continually a pestilent tongue in his dispraise.

The prince knew this, yet he was patient.

But at last he bethought him; and upon a wintry night there came to the door of the man a servant of the prince, bearing a sack of flour, a bag of soap and a cone of sugar.

And the servant said, "The prince sends you these gifts in token of remembrance."

The man was elated, for he thought the gifts were an homage from the prince. And in his pride he went to the bishop and told him what the prince had done, saying, "Can you not see how the prince desires my goodwill?"

But the bishop said, "Oh, how wise a prince, and how little you understand. He speaks in symbols. The flour is for your empty stomach; the soap is for your dirty hide; and the sugar is to sweeten your bitter tongue."

From that day forward the man became shy even of himself. His hatred of the prince was greater than ever, and even more he hated the bishop who had revealed the prince unto him.

But thereafter he kept silent.

PEACE AND WAR

Three dogs were basking in the sun and conversing.

The first dog said dreamily, "It is indeed wondrous to be living in this day of dogdom. Consider the ease with which we travel under the sea, upon the earth and even in the sky. And meditate for a moment upon the inventions brought forth for the comfort of dogs, even for our eyes and ears and noses."

And the second dog spoke and he said, "We are more heedful of the arts. We bark at the moon more rhythmically than did our forefathers. And when we gaze at ourselves in the water we see that our features are clearer that the features of yesterday."

Then the third dog spoke and said, "But what interests me most and beguiles my mind is the tranquil understanding existing between dogdoms."

At that very moment they looked, and lo, the dog-catcher was approaching.

The three dogs sprang up and scampered down the street; and as they ran the third dog said, "For God's sake, run for your lives. Civilisation is after us."

TEARS AND LAUGHTER

Upon the bank of the Nile at eventide, a hyena met a crocodile and they stopped and greeted one another.

The hyena spoke and said, "How goes the day with you, Sir?'

And the crocodile answered saying, "It goes badly with me. Sometimes in my pain and sorrow I weep, and then the creatures always say, 'They are but crocodile tears.' And this wounds me beyond all telling."

Then the hyena said, "You speak of your pain and your sorrow, but think of me also, for a moment. I gaze at the beauty of the world, its wonders and its miracles, and out of sheer joy I laugh even as the day laughs. And then the people of the jungle say, 'It is but the laughter of a hyena.'"

AT THE FAIR

There came to the Fair a girl from the countryside, most comely. There was a lily and a rose in her face. There was sunset in her hair, and dawn smiled upon her lips.

No sooner did the lovely stranger appear in their sight than the young men sought her and surrounded her. One would dance with her, and another would cut a cake in her honour. And they all desired to kiss her cheek. For after all, was it not the Fair?

But the girl was shocked and startled, and she thought ill of the young men. She rebuked them, and she even struck one or two of them in the face. Then she ran away from them.

And on her way home that evening she was saying in her heart, "I am disgusted. How unmannerly and ill bred are these men. It is beyond all patience."

A year passed during which that very comely girl thought much of Fairs and men. Then she came again to the Fair with the lily and the rose in her face, the sunset in her hair and the smile of dawn upon her lips.

But now the young men, seeing her, turned from her. And all the day long she was unsought and alone.

And at eventide as she walked the road toward her home she cried in her heart, "I am disgusted. How unmannerly and ill bred are these youths. It is all beyond patience."

THE SPEECHLESS ANIMAL

In the twilight of a beautiful day, when fancy seized upon my mind, I passed by the edge of the city and tarried before the wreck of an abandoned house of which only rubble was left.

In the rubble I saw a dog lying upon dirt and ashes. Sores covered his skin, and sickness racked his feeble body. Staring now and then at the setting sun, his sorrowful eyes expressed humiliation, despair, and misery.

I walked slowly toward him wishing that I knew animal speech so that I might console him with my sympathy. But my approach only terrified him, and he tried to rise on his palsied legs. Falling, he turned a look on me in which helpless wrath was mingled with supplication. In that glance was speech more lucid than man's and more moving than a woman's tears. This is what I understood him to say:

"Man, I have suffered through illness caused by your brutality and persecution.

"I have run from your bruising foot and taken refuge here, for dust and ashes are gentler than man's heart, these ruins less melancholy than the soul of man. Begone, you intruder from the world of misrule and injustice.

"I am a miserable creature who served the son of Adam with faith and loyalty. I was man's faithful companion, I guarded him day and night. I grieved during his absence and welcomed him with joy upon his return. I was contented with the crumbs that fell from his board, and happy with the bones that his teeth had stripped. But when I grew old and ill, he drove me from his home and left me to merciless boys of the alleys.

"Oh son of Adam, I see the similarity between me and your fellow men when age disables them. There are soldiers who fought for their country when they were in the prime of life, and who later tilled its soil. But now that the winter of their life has come and they are useful no longer, they are cast aside.

"I also see a resemblance between my lot and that of a woman who, during the days of her lovely maidenhood enlivened the heart of a young man; and who then, as a mother, devoted her life to her children. But now, grown old, she is ignored and avoided. How oppressive you are, son of Adam, and how cruel!"

Thus spoke the speechless animal whom my heart had understood.

COMMUNION OF SPIRITS

Awake, my love, awake! For my spirit hails you from beyond the seas, and offers you her wings above the raging waves.

Awake, for silence has halted the clamour of the horses' hoofs and the trap of the passers-by.

Slumber has embraced the spirits of men, while I alone remain awake; longing lifts me out of enveloping sleep.

Love brings me close to you but then, anxiety takes me far away.

I have left my bed, my love, for fear of the ghost of forgetfulness hiding in the quilts.

I have thrown my book aside, for my sighs silenced the words and left the pages blank before my eyes!

Awake, awake, my love, and hear me.

I hear you, my beloved! I heard you call from beyond the seas and felt the soft touch of your wings; I have left my bed and walked upon the grass and the night dew has wet my feet and the hem of my garment. Here I stand under the blossoms of the almond tree, heeding the call of your spirit.

Speak to me, my love, and let your breath mount the breeze that comes towards me from the valleys of Lebanon. Speak. No one hears but me. Night has taken all others to their resting places.

Heaven has woven a veil of moonlight and drawn it over all Lebanon, my beloved.

Heaven has fashioned from the shadows of night a thick cloak lined with the fumes of workshops and the breath of Death, and laid it over the frame of the city, my love.

The villagers have surrendered to Slumber in their huts in the midst of the willow and walnut trees. Their spirits have sped towards the land of dreams, my beloved.

Men are bent under the burden of gold, and the steep road of green weakens their knees. Their eyes are heavy with trouble and weariness, and they drop on their beds as a haven, my love, from the Ghosts of Fear and Despair.

The ghosts of past ages walk in the valleys, and the spirits of the kings and prophets hover over the knolls and the hills. And my thoughts, fashioned by memory, show me the might of the Chaldeans, the splendour of the Assyrians, and the nobility of the Arabs.

In the sinister alleys walk the grim spirits of the thieves; the heads of the vipers of lust appear from the crevices of the ramparts; and the ague of sickness, mingled with the agony of Death, shudders through the streets. Memory has removed the veil of forgetfulness from my eyes and shows me the loathsomeness of Sodom and the sins of Gomorrah.

The branches sway, my beloved, and their rustling joins the murmur of the rivulet in the valley, repeating to our ears the canticles of Solomon, the strains of David's harp, and the songs of Ishak al-Mausili.

The souls of the hungry children in the lodgings tremble; and the sighs of the mothers tossing upon the beds of misery and despair have reached the sky; and anxious dreams afflict the hearts of the infirm. I hear their bitter lamentations.

The fragrance of flowers has mingled with the pungent breath of the cedars. Brought by the frolicsome breeze over the hills, it fills the soul with affection and inspires longing for flight.

But the miasmas from the marshes also rise, steaming with disease. Like sharp secret arrows they have penetrated the senses and poisoned the air.

The morning has come, my beloved, and the soft fingers of wakefulness fondle the eyes of the dreamers. Rays of light force open the shutters and reveal Life's resolution and glory. The villages, reposing in peace and tranquillity upon the shoulders of the valley, rise from their slumber; church bells fill the air with their pleasing summons to morning prayer. And from the caves echo the chimes as if all Nature joins in reverent prayer. The calves have left their stalls, and the sheep and the goats their sheds, to graze upon the glittering, dewy grass. The shepherds walk before them, piping on their reeds; and behind them walk the damsels singing like the birds welcoming the morn.

And now the heavy hand of the Day lies upon the city. The curtains have been drawn from the windows and the doors are open. The fatigued eyes and drawn faces of toilers appear in the workshops. They feel death encroaching upon their lives, and on their shrivelled countenances appear Fear and Despair. The streets are congested with hurrying greedy souls; and everywhere are heard the clanking of iron, the rattling of wheels, and whistling of steam. The city has turned into a battlefield where the strong wrestle down the weak and the rich exploit and tyrannise over the poor.

How beautiful is life, my beloved; it is like the poet's heart, filled with light and tenderness.

And how cruel is life, my love, it is like a criminal's heart, throbbing with vice and fear.

WISDOM AND I

In the silence of the night, Wisdom came into my chamber and stood by my bed. She gazed upon me like a loving mother, dried my tears, and said:

"I have heard the cries of your soul, and have come here to comfort you. Open your heart to me and I shall fill it with light. Ask, and I shall show you the path of Truth."

I complied with her bidding, and asked:

"Who am I, Wisdom, and how came I to this place of horrors? What are these mighty hopes, these mountains of books, and these strange figures? What are these thoughts that come and go like a flock of doves? What are these words we compose with desire and write down in joy? What are these sorrowful and joyous conclusions that embrace my soul and envelope my heart? Whose are these eyes that stare at me and pierce the very inmost recesses of my soul, and yet are oblivious of my grief? What are these voices that lament the passing of my days and chant the praises of my childhood? Who is this youth that toys with my desires and mocks my feelings, forgetting the deeds of yesterday, contenting himself with the littleness of today, and arming himself against the slow approach of tomorrow?

"What is this dreadful world that moves me and to what unknown land?

"What is this earth that opens wide her jaws to swallow our bodies and prepares an everlasting shelter for greed? Who is this Man who contents himself with the favours of Fortune and craves a kiss from the lips of Life while Death smites him in the face? Who is this Man who buys a moment of pleasure with a year of repentance and gives himself over to sleep, while dreams call to him? Who is this Man who swims on the waves of Ignorance toward the gulf of Darkness?

"Tell me, Wisdom, what are all these things?"

And Wisdom opened her lips and spoke:

"You, Man, would see the world with the eyes of God, and would grasp the secrets of the hereafter by means of human thought. Such is the fruit of ignorance.

"Go into the field, and see how the bee hovers over the sweet flowers and the eagle swoops down on its prey. Go into your neighbour's house and see the infant child bewitched by the firelight, while the mother is busied at her tasks. Be like the bee, and do not waste your spring days gazing on the doings of the eagle. Be like the child rejoicing at the firelight and let the mother be. All that you see was, and still is, yours.

"The many books and strange figures and the lovely thoughts around you are ghosts of the spirits that have been before you. The words your lips utter are the links in the chain that you and your fellow men. The sorrowful and joyful conclusions are the seeds sown by the past in the field of your soul to be reaped by the future.

"The youth that toys with your desires is he who will open the gate of your heart for Light to enter. The earth that opens wide her mouth to swallow man and his works is the redeemer of our souls from bondage to our bodies.

"The world that moves with you is your heart, which is the world itself. And Man, whom you deem so small and ignorant, is God's messenger who has come to learn the joy of life through sorrow and gain knowledge from ignorance."

Thus spoke Wisdom, and laid a hand upon my burning brow, saying:

"March on. Do not tarry. To go forward is to move toward perfection. March on, and fear not the thorns or the sharp stones of Life's path."

LOVE AND YOUTH

A youth in the dawn of life sat at his desk in a solitary house. Now he looked through the window at the sky that was studded with glittering stars, now he turned his gaze toward a maiden's picture, which he held in his hand. Its lines and colours were worthy of a master; they became reflected in the youth's mind, and opened to him the secrets of the World and the mystery of Eternity.

The picture of the woman called to the youth, and at the moment turned his eyes into ears, so that he understood the language of the spirits that hovered over the room, and his heart became seared with love.

Thus the hours passed as if they were only a moment of some beautiful dream, or only a year in a life of Eternity.

Then the youth set the picture before him, took up his pen, and poured out his heart's feelings upon the parchment:

"Beloved: Great truth that transcends Nature does not pass from one being to another by way of human speech. Truth chooses Silence to convey her meaning to loving souls.

"I know that the silence of the night is the worthiest messenger between our two hearts, for she bears Love's message and recites the psalms of our hearts. Just as God has made our souls prisoners of our bodies, so Love has made me a prisoner of words and speech.

"They say, O Beloved, that Love is a devouring flame in the heart of man. I knew at our first meeting that I had known you for ages, and I knew at the time of parting that nothing was strong enough to keep us apart.

"My first glimpse of you was not in truth the first. The hour in which our hearts met confirmed in me the belief in Eternity and in the immortality of the Soul.

"At such a moment Nature lifts the veil from him who believes himself oppressed, and reveals her everlasting justice.

"Do you recall the brook by which we sat and gazed at each other, Beloved? Do you know your eyes told me at that moment that your love was not born of pity but of justice? And now I can proclaim to myself and to the world that the gifts which derive from justice are greater that those that spring from charity.

"And I can say too that Love which is the child of chance is like the stagnant waters of the marshes.

"Beloved, before me stretches a life which I can fashion into greatness and beauty—a life that began with our first meeting, and which will last to eternity.

"For I know that it is within you to bring forth the power that God has bestowed upon me, to be embodied in great words and deeds, even as the sun brings to life the fragrant flowers of the field.

"And thus, my love for you shall endure for ever."

The youth rose and walked slowly and reverently across the room. He looked through the window and saw the moon rising above the horizon and filling the spacious sky with her gentle radiance.

Then he returned to his desk and wrote:

"Forgive me, my Beloved, for speaking to you in the second person. For you are my other, beautiful, half, which I have lacked ever since we emerged from the sacred hand of God. Forgive me, my Beloved!"

THE LISTENER

Oh Wind, you who pass by us, now singing sweetly and softly, now sighing and lamenting: we hear you, but we cannot see you. We feel your touch, but we cannot descry your shape. You are like an ocean of love that engulfs our spirits, but does not drown them.

You ascend with the hills, and descend with the valleys, diffusing yourself over field and meadow. There is strength in your ascent and gentleness in your descent; and grace in your dispersion. You are like a merciful king, gracious toward the oppressed, but stern toward the arrogant and strong.

In Autumn you moan through the valleys, and the trees echo your wailing. In Winter you break your chains, and all Nature rebels with you.

In Spring you stir from your slumbers, still weak and infirm, and through your faint stirrings the fields begin to awake.

In Summer you hide behind the veil of Silence as if you had died, smitten by the shafts of the sun and the spears of heat.

Were you indeed lamenting in the late Autumn days, or were you laughing at the blushes of the naked trees? Were you angry in Winter, or were you dancing around the snow-decked tomb of Night?

Were you indeed languishing in the Spring, or were you grieving for the loss of your beloved, the Youth of all seasons?

Were you perchance dead in those Summer days, or were

you only asleep in the heart of the fruits, in the eyes of the vineyards, or in the ears of the wheat upon the threshing floors?

From the streets of the cities you raise up and bear the seeds of plagues; and from the hills you waft the fragrant breath of flowers. Thus the great Soul sustains the sorrow of Life and silently meets its joys.

Into the ears of the rose you whisper a secret whose meaning she grasps; often she is troubled—then she rejoices. Such is the way of God with the soul of Man.

Now you tarry. Now you hasten here and yonder, moving ceaselessly. Such too is the mind of Man, who lives when he acts and dies when he is idle.

You write your songs on the face of the waters; then you erase them. So does the poet when he is creating.

From the South you come as warm as Love; and from the North as cold as Death. From the East as gentle as the touch of the Soul; and from the West as fierce as Wrath and Fury. Are you as fickle as Age, or are you the courier of weighty tidings from the four points of the compass?

You rage through the desert, you trample the innocent caravans underfoot and bury them in mountains of sand. Are you that same frolicsome breeze that trembles with the dawn among the leaves and branches and flits like a dream through the windings of the valleys where the flowers bow in greeting and where the grass droops heavy-lidded with the intoxication of your breath?

You rise from the oceans and shake their silent depths from your tresses, and in your rage you lay waste ships and crews. Are you that selfsame gentle breeze that caresses the locks of children as they play around their homes?

Whither do you carry our hearts, our sighs, our breaths, our smiles? What do you do with the flying torches of our souls? Do you bear them beyond the horizon of Life? Do you drag them like sacrificial victims to distant and horrible caves to destroy them?

In the still night, hearts reveal their secrets to you. And at dawn, eyes open at your gentle touch. Are you mindful of what the heart has felt or the eyes have seen?

Between your wings the anguished lays the echo of his mournful songs, the orphan the fragments of his broken heart, and the oppressed his painful sighs. Within the folds of your mantle the stranger lays his longing, the forsaken his burden, and the fallen woman her despair.

Do you preserve all these in safekeeping for the humble? Or are you like Mother Earth, who entombs all that she brings forth?

Do you hear these cries and lamentations? Do you hear these moans and sighs? Or are you like the proud and mighty who do not see the outstretched hand or hear the cries of the poor?

O Life of all Listeners, do you hear?

FACES

I have seen a face with a thousand countenances, and a face that was but a single countenance as if held in a mould.

I have seen a face whose sheen I could look through to the ugliness beneath, and a face whose sheen I had to lift to see how beautiful it was.

I have seen an old face much lined with nothing, and a smooth face in which all things were graven.

I know faces, because I look through the fabric my own eye weaves, and behold the reality beneath.

THE HERMIT AND THE BEASTS

Once there lived among the green hills a hermit. He was pure of spirit and white of heart. And all the animals of the land and all the fowls of the air came to him in pairs and he spoke unto them. They heard him gladly, and they would gather near unto him, and would not go until night fall, when he would send them away, entrusting them to the wind and the woods with his blessing.

Upon an evening as he was speaking of love, a leopard raised her head and said to the hermit, "You speak to us of loving. Tell us, Sir, where is your mate?"

And the hermit said, "I have no mate."

Then a great cry of surprise rose from the company of beasts and fowls, and they began to say among themselves, "How can he tell us of loving and mating when he himself knows naught thereof?" And quietly and in disdain they left him alone.

That night the hermit lay upon his mat with his face earthward, and he wept bitterly and beat his hands upon his breast.

THE SHADOW

Upon a June day the grass said to the shadow of an elm tree, "You move to right and left over-often, and you disturb my peace."

And the shadow answered and said, "Not I, not I. Look skyward. There is a tree that moves in the wind to the east and to the west, between the sun and the earth."

And the grass looked up, and for the first time beheld the tree. And it said in its heart, "Why, behold, there is a larger grass than myself."

And the grass was silent.

THE CRIMINAL

A young man of strong body, weakened by hunger, sat on the walker's portion of the street stretching his hand toward all who passed, begging and repeating the sad song of his defeat in life, while suffering from hunger and from humiliation.

When night came, his lips and tongue were parched, while his hand was still as empty as his stomach.

He gathered himself and went out from the city, where he sat under a tree and wept bitterly. Then he lifted his puzzled eyes to heaven while hunger was eating his inside, and he said, "Oh Lord, I went to the rich man and asked for employment, but he turned away because of my shabbiness; I knocked at the school door, but was forbidden solace because I was empty-handed; I sought any occupation that would give me bread, but all to no avail. In desperation I asked alms, but Thy worshippers saw me and said, "He is strong and lazy, and he should not beg."

"Oh Lord, it is Thy will that my mother gave birth unto me, and now the earth offers me back to You before Ending."

His expression then changed. He arose and his eyes now glittered in determination. He fashioned a thick and heavy stick from the branch of the tree, and pointed it toward the city, shouting, "I asked for bread with all the strength of my voice, and was refused. Now I shall obtain it by the strength of my muscles! I asked for bread in the name of mercy and love, but humanity did not heed. I shall take it now in the name of evil!"

The passing years rendered the youth a robber, killer,

and destroyer of souls; he crushed all who opposed him; he amassed fabulous wealth with which he won himself over to those in power. He was admired by colleagues, envied by other thieves, and feared by the multitudes.

His riches and false position prevailed upon the Emir to appoint him deputy in that city—the sad process pursued by unwise governors. Thefts were then legalised; oppression was supported by authority; crushing of the weak became commonplace; the throngs curried and praised.

Thus does the first touch of humanity's selfishness make criminals of the humble, and make killers of the sons of peace; thus does the early greed of humanity grow and strike back at humanity a thousandfold!

THE PATH

There lived among the hills a woman and her son, and he was her first-born and her only child.

And the boy died of a fever whilst the physician stood by.

The mother was distraught with sorrow, and she cried to the physician and besought him saying, "Tell me, tell me, what was it that made quiet his striving and silent song?"

And the physician said, "It was the fever."

And the mother said, "What is the fever?"

And the physician answered, "I cannot explain it. It is a thing infinitely small that visits the body, and we cannot see it with our human eye."

Then the physician left her. And she kept repeating to herself, "something infinitely small. We cannot see it with our human eye."

And at evening the priest came to console her. And she wept and she cried out saying, "Oh, why have I lost my son, my only son, my first-born?"

And the priest answered, "My child, it is the will of God."

And the woman said, "What is God and where is God? I would see God that I may tear my bosom before Him, and pour the blood of my heart at His feet. Tell me where I shall find Him."

And the priest said, "God is infinitely vast. He is not to be seen with our human eye."

Then the woman cried out, "The infinitely small has slain my son through the will of the infinitely great! Then what are we? What are we?"

At that moment the woman's mother came into the room with the shroud for the dead boy, and she heard the words of the priest and also her daughter's cry. And she laid down the shroud, and took her daughter's hand in her own hand, and she said, "My daughter, we ourselves are the infinitely small and the infinitely great; and we are the path between the two."

THE SEVEN SELVES

In the stillest hour of the night, as I lay half asleep, my seven selves sat together and thus conversed in whispers:

First Self: Here, in this madman, I have dwelt all these years, with naught to do but renew his pain by day and recreate his sorrow by night. I can bear my fate no longer, and now I rebel.

Second Self: Yours is a better lot than mine, brother, for it is given me to be this madman's joyous self. I laugh his laughter and sing his happy hours, and with thrice winged feet I dance his brighter thoughts. It is I that would rebel against my weary existence.

Third Self: And what of me, the love ridden self, the flaming brand of wild passion and fantastic desires? It is I the love-sick who would rebel against this madman.

Fourth Self: I, amongst you all, am the most miserable, for naught was given me but odious hatred and destructive loathing. It is I, the tempest-like self, the one born in the black caves of Hell, who would protest against serving this madman.

Fifth Self: Nay, it is I, the thinking self, the fanciful self, the self of hunger and thirst, the one doomed to wander without rest in search of unknown things and things not yet created; it is I, not you, who would rebel.

Sixth Self: And I, the working self, the pitiful labourer, who, with patient hands, and longing eyes, fashion the days into images and give the formless elements new and eternal forms—it is I, the solitary one, who would rebel against this restless madman.

Seventh Self: How strange that you all would rebel against this man, because each and every one of you has a preordained fate to fulfil. Ah! could I but be like one of you, a self with a determined lot! But I have none, I am the do-nothing self, the one who sits in the dumb, empty nowhere and nowhen, while you are busy re-creating life. Is it you or I, neighbours, who should rebel?

When the seventh self thus spake the other six selves looked with pity upon him but said nothing more; and as the night grew deeper one after the other went to sleep enfolded with a new and happy submission.

But the seventh self remained watching and gazing at nothingness, which is behind all things.

THE GREATER SEA

My soul and I went to the great sea to bathe. And when we reached the shore, we went about looking for a hidden and lonely place.

But as we walked, we saw a man sitting on a grey rock taking pinches of salt from a bag and throwing them into the sea.

"This is the pessimist," said my soul, "Let us leave this place. We cannot bathe here."

We walked on until we reached an inlet. There we saw, standing on a white rock, a man holding a bejewelled box, from which he took sugar and threw it into the sea.

"And this is the optimist," said my soul, "And he too must not see our naked bodies."

Further on we walked. And on a beach we saw a man picking up dead fish and tenderly putting them back into the water.

And we cannot bathe before him," said my soul. "He is the humane philanthropist."

And we passed on.

Then we came where we saw a man tracing his shadow on the sand. Great waves came and erased it. But he went on tracing it again and again.

"He is the mystic," said my soul, "Let us leave him."

And we walked on, till in a quiet cove we saw a man scooping up the foam and putting it into an alabaster bowl.

"He is the idealist," said my soul, "Surely he must not see our nudity."

And on we walked. Suddenly we heard a voice crying, "This is the sea. This is the deep sea. This is the vast and mighty sea." And when we reached the voice it was a man whose back was turned to the sea, and at his ear he held a shell, listening to its murmur.

And my soul said, "Let us pass on. He is the realist, who turns his back on the whole he cannot grasp, and busies himself with a fragment."

So we passed on. And in a weedy place among the rocks was a man with his head buried in the sand. And I said to my soul, "We can bathe here, for he cannot see us."

"Nay," said my soul, "For he is the most deadly of them all. He is the puritan."

Then a great sadness came over the face of my soul, and into her voice.

"Let us go hence," she said, "For there is no lonely, hidden place where we can bathe. I would not have this wind lift my golden hair, or bare my white bosom in this air, or let the light disclose my sacred nakedness."

Then we left that sea to seek the Greater Sea.

THE WHITE TORCH

The month of Nisan had nearly passed. I continued to visit the home of Farris Effendi and to meet Selma in that beautiful garden, gazing upon her beauty, marvelling at her intelligence, and hearing the stillness of sorrow. I felt an invisible hand drawing me to her.

Every visit gave me a new meaning to her beauty and a new insight into her sweet spirit, until she became a book whose pages I could understand and whose praises I could sing, but which I could never finish reading. A woman whom Providence has provided with beauty of spirit and body is a truth, at the same time both open and secret, which we can understand only by love, and touch only by virtue; and when we attempt to describe such a woman she disappears like a vapour.

Selma Karamy had bodily and spiritual beauty, but how can I describe her to one who never knew her? Can a dead man remember the singing of a nightingale and the fragrance of a rose and the sigh of a brook? Can a prisoner who is heavily loaded with shackles follow the breeze of the dawn? Is not silence more painful than death? Does pride prevent me from describing Selma in plain words since I cannot draw her truthfully with luminous colours? A hungry man in a desert will not refuse to eat dry bread if Heaven does not shower him with manna and quails.

In her white silk dress, Selma was slender as a ray of moonlight coming through the window. She walked gracefully and rhythmically. Her voice was low and sweet; words fell from her lips like drops of dew falling from the petals of flowers when they are disturbed by the wind.

But Selma's face! No words can describe its expression, reflecting first great internal suffering, then heavenly exaltation.

The beauty of Selma's face was not classic; it was like a dream of revelation which cannot be measured or bound or copied by the brush of a painter, or the chisel of a sculptor. Selma's beauty was not in her golden hair, but in the virtue and purity which surrounded it; not in her large eyes, but in the light which emanated from them; not in her red lips, but in the sweetness of her words; not in her ivory neck, but in its slight bow to the front. Nor was it in her perfect figure, but in the nobility of her spirit, burning like a white torch between earth and sky. Her beauty was like a gift of poetry. But poets are unhappy people, for, no matter how high their spirits reach, they will still be enclosed in an envelope of tears.

Selma was deeply thoughtful rather than talkative, and her silence was a kind of music that carried one to a world of dreams and made him listen to the throbbing of his heart, and see the ghosts of his thoughts and feelings standing before him, looking him in the eyes.

She wore a cloak of deep sorrow through her life, which increased her strange beauty and dignity, as a tree in blossom is more lovely when seen through the mist of dawn.

Sorrow linked her spirit and mine, as if each saw in the other's face what the heart was feeling and heard the echo of a hidden voice. God had made two bodies in one, and separation could be nothing but agony.

The sorrowful spirit finds rest when united with a similar one. They join affectionately, as a stranger is cheered when he sees another stranger in a strange land. Hearts that are united through the medium of sorrow will not be separated by the glory of happiness. Love that is cleansed by tears will remain eternally pure and beautiful.

THE POET

I am a stranger in this world, and there is a severe solitude and painful lonesomeness in my exile. I am alone, but in my aloneness I contemplate an unknown and enchanting country, and this meditation fills my dreams with spectres of a great and distant land which my eyes have never seen.

I am a stranger among my people and I have no friends. When I see a person I say within myself, "Who is he, and in what manner do I know him, and why is he here, and what law has joined me with him?"

I am a stranger to myself, and when I hear my tongue speak, my ears wonder over my voice; I see my inner self smiling, crying, braving, and fearing; and my existence wonders over my substance while my soul interrogates my heart; but I remain unknown, engulfed by tremendous silence.

My thoughts are strangers to my body, and as I stand before the mirror, I see something in my face which my soul does not see, and I find in my eyes what my inner self does not find.

When I walk vacant-eyed through the streets of the clamorous city, the children follow me, shouting, "Here is a blind man! Let us give him a walking cane to feel his way." When I run from them, I meet with a group of maidens, and they grasp the edges of my garment, saying, "He is deaf like the rock; let us fill his ears with the music of love." And when I flee from them, a throng of aged people point at me with trembling fingers and say, "He is a madman who lost his mind in the world of genii and ghouls."

I am a stranger in this world; I roamed the Universe from end to end, but could not find a place to rest my head; nor did I know any human I confronted, neither an individual who would hearken to my mind.

When I open my sleepless eyes at dawn, I find myself imprisoned in a dark cave from whose ceiling hang the insects and upon whose floor crawl the vipers.

When I go out to meet the light, the shadow of my body follows me, but the shadow of my spirit precedes me and leads the way to an unknown place seeking things beyond my understanding, and grasping objects that are meaningless to me.

At eventide I return and lie upon my bed, made of soft feathers and lined with thorns, and I contemplate and feel the troublesome and happy desires, and sense the painful and joyous hopes.

At midnight the ghosts of the past ages and the spirits of the forgotten civilisation enter through the crevices of the cave to visit me... I stare at them and they gaze upon me; I talk to them and they answer me smilingly. Then I endeavour to clutch them, but they sift through my fingers and vanish like the mist which rests on the lake.

I am a stranger in this world, and there is no one in the Universe who understands the language I speak. Patterns of bizarre remembrance form suddenly in my mind, and my eyes bring forth queer images and sad ghosts. I walk in the deserted prairies, watching the streamlets running fast, up and up from the depths of the valley to the top of the mountain; I watch the naked trees blooming and bearing fruit, and shedding their leaves in one instant, and then I see the branches fall and turn into speckled snakes. I see the birds hovering above, singing and wailing; then they stop and open their wings and turn into undraped maidens with long hair, looking at me from behind kohled and infatuated eyes, and smiling at me with full lips soaked with honey, stretching their scented hands toward me. Then they ascend and disappear from my sight like phantoms, leaving in the firmament the resounding echo of their taunts and mocking laughter.

I am a stranger in this world... I am a poet who composes what life proses, and who proses what life composes.

For this reason I am a stranger, and I shall remain a stranger until the white and friendly wings of Death carry me home into my beautiful country. There, where light and peace and understanding abide, I will await the other strangers who will be rescued by the friendly trap of time from this narrow, dark world.

THE TEMPEST

PART I

Yusif El Fakhri was thirty years of age when he withdrew himself from society and departed to live in an isolated hermitage in the vicinity of Kedeesha Valley in North Lebanon. The people of the nearby villages heard various tales concerning Yusif; some related that his was a wealthy and noble family, and that he loved a woman who betrayed him and caused him to lead a solitary life, while others said that he was a poet who deserted the clamorous city and retired to that place in order to record his thoughts and compose his inspiration; and many were sure that he was a mystic who was contented with the spiritual world, although most people insisted that he was a madman.

As for myself, I could not draw any conclusion regarding the man, for I knew that there must be a deep secret within his heart whose revelation I would not trust to mere speculation. I had long hoped for the opportunity to meet this strange man. I had endeavoured in devious ways to win his friendship in order to study his reality and learn his story by inquiring as to his purpose in life, but my efforts were in vain. When I met him for the first time, he was walking by the forest of the Holy Cedars of Lebanon, and I greeted him with the finest choice of words, but he returned my greeting by merely shaking his head and striding off.

On another occasion I found him standing in the midst of a small vineyard by a monastery, and again I approached and greeted him, saying, "It is said by the villagers that this monastery was built by a Syriac group in the Fourteenth

Century; do you know anything of its history?" He replied coldly, "I do not know who built this monastery, nor do I care to know." And he turned his back to me and added, "Why do you not ask your grandparents, who are older than I, and who know more of the history of these valleys than I do?" Realising at once my utter failure, I left him.

Thus did two years pass, and the bizarre life of this strange man preyed on my mind and disturbed my dreams.

PART II

One day in Autumn, as I was roaming the hills and knolls adjacent to the hermitage of Yusif El Fakhri, I was suddenly caught in a strong wind and torrent rain, and the tempest cast me here and there like a boat whose rudder has been broken and whose masts have been torn by a gale in a rough sea. I directed my steps with difficulty toward Yusif's place, saying to myself, "This is an opportunity I have long sought, and the tempest will be my excuse for entering, while my wet clothes will serve as good reason for lingering."

I was in a miserable plight when I reached the hermitage, and as I knocked on the door, the man whom I had been longing to see opened it. He was holding in one hand a dying bird whose head had been injured and whose wings had been broken. I greeted him saying, "I beg your forgiveness for this annoying intrusion. The raging tempest trapped me while I was afar from home." He frowned, saying, "There are many caves in this wilderness in which you might have taken refuge." However, he did not close the door, and the beat of my heart quickened in anticipation, for the realisation of my great wish was close at hand. He commenced to touch the bird's head gently and with the utmost care and interest, exhibiting a quality important to my heart. I was surprised over the two opponent characteristics I found in that man—mercy and cruelty at the same time. We became aware of the strained silence. He resented my presence, I desired to remain.

It seemed as if he felt my thought, for he looked up and said, "The tempest is clean, and declines to eat soured meat. Why do you seek to escape from it?" And with a touch of humour, I responded, " The tempest may not desire salted or soured things, but she is inclined to chill and tender all things, and undoubtedly she would enjoy consuming me if she grasped me again." His expression was severe when he retorted, "The tempest would have bestowed upon you a great honour, of which you are not worthy, if she had swallowed you." I agreed, "Yes, Sir, I fled the tempest so I might not be awarded an honour which I do not merit." He turned his face from me in an effort to choke his smile, and then motioned toward a wooden bench by the fireplace and invited me to rest and dry my raiment. I could scarcely control my elation.

I thanked him and sat down while he seated himself opposite, on a bench carved of rock. He commenced to dip his finger tips into an earthenware jar containing a kind of oil, applying it softly to the bird's head and wings. Without looking up he said, "The strong winds have caused this bird to fall upon the rocks between Life and Death." I replied, rendering comparison, "And the strong winds have sent me, adrift, to your door, in time to prevent having my head injured and my wings broken."

He looked at me seriously and said, "It is my wish that man

would show the bird's instinct, and it is my wish that the tempest would break the people's wings. For man inclines toward fear and cowardice, and as he feels the awakening of the tempest he crawls into the crevices and the caves of the earth and hides himself."

My purpose was to extract the story of his self-imposed exile, and I provoked, "Yes, the birds possess an honour and courage that man does not possess... Man lives in the shadow of laws and customs which he made and fashioned for himself, but the birds live according to the same free Eternal Law which causes the earth to pursue its mighty path about the sun." His eyes and face brightened, as if he had found in me an understanding disciple, and he exclaimed, "Well done! If you place belief in your own words you should leave civilisation and its corrupt laws and traditions, and live like the birds in a place empty of all things except the magnificent law of heaven and earth.

"Believing is a fine thing, but placing those beliefs into execution is a test of strength. Many are those who talk like the roar of the sea, but their lives are shallow and stagnant, like the rotting marshes. Many are those who lift their heads above the mountain tops, but their spirits remain dormant in the obscurity of the caverns." He rose trembling from his seat and placed the bird upon a folded cloth by the window.

He placed a bundle of dry sticks upon the fire, saying, "Remove your sandals and warm your feet, for dampness is dangerous to man's health. Dry well your garments, and be comfortable."

Yusif's continued hospitality kept my hopes high. I approached near to the fire, and the steam sifted from my wet robe. While he stood at the door gazing at the grey skies, my mind searched for the opening wedge into his background. I asked, innocently, "Has it been long since you came to this place?"

Without looking at me, he answered quietly, "I came to this place when the earth was without form, and void; and darkness was upon the face of the deep. And the Spirit of God moved upon the face of the waters."

I was aghast at these words! Struggling to gather my shocked and scattered wits, I said to myself, "How fantastic this man is! And how difficult is the path that leads to his reality! But I shall attack cautiously and slowly and patiently, until his reticence turns into communication, and his strangeness into understanding."

PART III

Night was spreading her black garment upon those valleys, and the tempest was shrieking dizzily and the rain becoming stronger. I began to fancy that the Biblical flood was coming again, to abolish life and wash man's filth from God's earth.

It seemed that the revolution of elements had created in Yusif's heart a tranquillity which often comes as a reaction to temperament and converts aloneness into conviviality. He ignited two candles, and then placed before me a jar of wine and a large tray containing bread, cheese, olives, honey, and some dry fruits. Then he sat near me, and after apologising for the small quantity—but not for the simplicity—of the food, asked me to join him.

We partook of the repast in understanding silence, listening to the wailing of the wind and the crying of the rain, and at the same time I was contemplating his face and trying to dig out his secrets, meditating the possible motive underlying his unusual existence. Having finished, he took a copper kettle from the fire and poured pure, aromatic coffee into two cups; then he opened a small box and offered me a cigarette, addressing me as "Brother." I took one while drinking my coffee, not believing what my eyes were seeing. He looked at me smilingly, and after he had inhaled deeply of his cigarette and sipped some coffee, he said, "Undoubtedly you are thinking upon the existence here of wine and tobacco and coffee, and you may also be wondering over my food and comforts. Your curiosity is justified in all respects, for you are one of the many who believe that in being away form the people, one is absent from life, and must abstain from all its enjoyment." Quickly I agreed, "Yes, it is related by the wise men that he who deserts the world for the purpose of worshipping God alone will leave behind all the enjoyment and plenty of life, contenting himself with the simple products of God alone, and existing on plants and water."

After a pause, heavy with thought, he mused, "I could have worshipped God while living among His creatures, for worship does not require solitude. I did not leave the people in order to see God, for I had always seen Him at the home of my father and mother. I deserted the people because their natures were in conflict with mine, and their dreams did not agree with my dreams... I left man because I found that the wheel of my soul was turning one way and grinding harshly against the wheels of other souls which were turning in the opposite direction. I left civilisation because I found it to be an old and corrupt tree, strong and terrible, whose roots are locked into the obscurity of the earth and whose branches are reaching beyond the cloud; but its blossoms are of greed and evil and crime, and its fruit is of woe and misery and fear. Crusaders have undertaken to blend good into it and change its nature, but they could not succeed. They died disappointed, persecuted and torn."

Yusif leaned toward the side of the fireplace as if awaiting the impression of his words upon my heart. I thought it best to remain a listener, and he continued, "No, I did not seek solitude to pray and lead a hermit's life... for prayer, which is the song of the heart, will reach the ears of God even when mingled with the shout and cry of thousands of voices. To live the life of a recluse is to torture the body and soul and deaden the inclinations, a kind of existence which is repugnant to me, for God has erected the bodies as temples for the spirits, and it is our mission to deserve and maintain the trust reposed in us by God.

"No, my brother, I did not seek solitude for religious purposes, but solely to avoid the people and their laws, their teachings and their traditions, their ideas and their clamour and their wailing.

"I sought solitude in order to keep from seeing the faces of men who sell themselves and buy with the same price that which is lower than they are, spiritually and materially.

"I sought solitude in order that I might not encounter the women who walk proudly, with one thousand smiles upon their lips, while in the depths of their thousands of hearts there is but one purpose.

"I sought solitude in order to conceal myself from those self-satisfied individuals who see the spectre of knowledge in their dreams and believe that they have attained their goal.

"I fled from society to avoid those who see but the phantom of truth in their awakening, and shout to the world that they have acquired completely the essence of truth.

"I deserted the world and sought solitude because I became tired of rendering courtesy to those multitudes who believe that humility is a sort of weakness, and mercy a kind of cowardice, and snobbery a form of strength.

"I sought solitude because my soul wearied of association with those who believe sincerely that the sun and moon and stars do not rise save from their coffers, and do not set except in their gardens.

"I ran from the office-seekers who shatter the earthly fate of the people while throwing into their eyes the golden dust and filling their ears with sounds of meaningless talk.

"I departed from the ministers who do not live according to their sermons, and who demand of the people that which they do not solicit of themselves.

"I sought solitude because I never obtained kindness from a human unless I paid the full price with my heart.

"I sought solitude because I loathe that great and terrible institution which the people call civilisation—that symmetrical monstrosity erected upon the perpetual misery of human kinds.

"I sought solitude for in it there is a full life for the spirit and for the heart and for the body. I found the endless prairies where the light of the sun rests, and where the flowers breathe their fragrance into space, and where the streams sing their way to the sea. I discovered the mountains where I found the fresh awakening of Spring, and the colourful longing of Summer, and the rich songs of

Autumn, and the beautiful mystery of Winter. I came to this far corner of God's domain for I hungered to learn the secrets of the Universe, and approach close to the throne of God."

Yusif breathed deeply, as if he had been relieved of a heavy burden. His eyes shone with strange and magical rays, and upon his radiant face appeared the signs of pride, will, and contentment.

A few minutes passed, and I was gazing placidly at him, and pondering the unveiling of what had been hidden from me; then I addressed him, saying, "You are undoubtedly correct in most of the things you have said, but through your diagnosis of the social ailment, you prove at the same time that you are a good doctor. I believe that the sick society is in dire need of such a physician, who should cure it or kill it. This distressed world begs your attention. Is it just or merciful to withdraw yourself from the ailing patient and deny him your benefit?"

He stared at me thoughtfully, and then said with futility, "Since the beginning of the world, the doctors have been trying to save the people from their disorders; some used knives, while others used potions, but pestilence spread hopelessly. It is my wish that the patient would content himself with remaining in his filthy bed, meditating his long-continued sores; but instead, he stretches his hands from under the robe and clutches at the neck of each who comes to visit him, choking him to death. What irony it is! The evil patient kills the doctor, and then closes his eyes and says within himself, "He was a great physician.' No, Brother, no one on earth can benefit humanity. The sower, however wise and expert he may be, cannot cause the field to sprout in Winter."

And I argued, "The people's Winter will pass away, and then comes the beautiful Spring, and the flowers must surely bloom in the fields, and the brooks will again leap in the valleys."

He frowned, and said bitterly, "Alas! Has God divided man's life—which is the whole creation—into seasons like those of the year? Will any tribe of human beings, living now in God's truth and spirit, desire to re-appear on the face of this earth? Will ever the time come when man settles and abides at the right arm of Life, rejoicing with the brilliant light of day and the peaceful silence of night? Can that dream become reality? Can it materialise after the earth has been covered with human flesh and drenched with man's blood?"

And Yusif stood and raised his hand toward the sky, as if pointing at a different world, and he continued, "This is naught but a vain dream for the world, but I am finding its accomplishment for myself, and what I am discovering here occupies every space in my heart and in the valleys and in the mountains." He now raised his intense voice, "What I really know to be true is the crying of my inner self. I am here living, and in the depths of my existence there is a thirst and hunger, and I find joy in partaking of the bread and wine of Life from the vases which I make and fashion by my own hands. For this reason I abandoned the boards of the people and came to this place, and I shall remain here until the Ending!"

He continued walking back and forth across the room in agitation while I was pondering his sayings and meditating the description of society's gaping wounds. I ventured again a tactful criticism. "I hold the utmost regard for your opinion and intentions, and I envy and respect your solitude and aloneness, but I know that this miserable nation has sustained a great loss in your expatriation, for she is in need of an understanding healer to help her through her difficulties and awaken her spirit."

He shook his head slowly and said, "This nation is like all the nations. And the people are made of the same element and do not vary except in their exterior appearance, which is of no consequence. The misery of our Oriental nations is the misery of the world, and what you call civilisation in the West is naught but another spectre of the many phantoms of tragic deception.

"Hypocrisy will always remain, even if her finger tips are coloured and polished; and Deceit will never change even if her touch becomes soft and delicate; and Falsehood will never turn into Truth even if you dress her with silken robes and place her in the palace; and Greed will not become contentment; nor will Crime become Virtue. And Eternal Slavery to teaching, to customs, and to history will remain Slavery even if she paints her face and disguises her voice. Slavery will remain Slavery in all her horrible form, even if she calls herself Liberty.

"No, my brother, the West is not higher than the East, nor is the West lower than the East, and the difference that stands between the two is not greater than the difference between the tiger and the lion. There is a just and perfect law that I have found behind the exterior of society, which equalises misery, prosperity, and ignorance; it does not prefer one nation to another, nor does it oppress one tribe in order to enrich another."

I exclaimed, "Then civilisation is vanity, and all in it is vanity!" He quickly responded, "Yes, civilisation is vanity and all in it is vanity... Inventions and discoveries are but amusement and comfort for the body when it is tired and weary. The conquest of distance and the victory over the seas are but false fruit which do not satisfy the soul, nor nourish the heart, neither lift the spirit, for they are afar from nature. And those structures and theories which man calls knowledge and art are naught except shackles and golden chains which man drags, and he rejoices with their glittering reflections and ringing sounds. They are strong cages whose bars man commenced fabricating ages ago, unaware that he was building from the inside, and that he would soon become his own prisoner to eternity. Yes, vain are the deeds of man, and vain are his purposes, and all is vanity upon this earth." He paused, then slowly added, "And among all vanities of life, there is only one thing that the spirit loves and craves. One thing dazzling and alone."

"What is it?" I inquired with quivering voice. He looked at me for a long minute and then closes his eyes. He placed his hands on his chest, while his face brightened, and with a serene and sincere voice he said, "It is an awakening in the spirit; it is an awakening in the inner depths of the heart; it is an overwhelming and magnificent power that descends suddenly upon man's conscience and opens his eyes, whereupon he sees Life amid a dizzying shower of brilliant music, surrounded by a circle of great light, with man standing as a pillar of beauty between the earth and the firmament. It is a flame that suddenly rages within the spirit and sears and purifies the heart, ascending above the earth and hovering in the spacious sky. It is a kindness that envelops the individual's heart whereby he would bewilder and disapprove all who opposed it, and revolt against those who refuse to understand its great meaning. It is a secret hand which removed the veil from my eyes while I was a member of society amidst my family, my friends and my countrymen.

"Many times I wondered, and spoke to myself, saying, 'What is this Universe, and why am I different from those people who are looking at me, and how do I know them, and where did I meet them, and why am I living among them? Am I a stranger among them, or is it they who are strange to this earth, built by Life who entrusted me with the keys?'"

He suddenly became silent, as if remembering something he had seen long before, refusing to reveal it. Then he stretched his arms forward and whispered, "That is what happened to me four years ago, when I left the world and came to this void place to live in the awakeness of life and enjoy kind thoughts and beautiful silence."

He walked toward the door, looking at the depths of the darkness as if preparing to address the tempest. But he spoke in a vibrating voice, saying, "It is an awakening within the spirit; he who knows it, is unable to reveal it by words; and he who knows it not, will never think upon the compelling and beautiful mystery of existence."

PART IV

An hour had passed and Yusif El Fakhri was striding about the room, stopping at random and gazing at the tremendous grey skies. I remained silent, reflecting upon the strange unison of joy and sorrow in his solitary life.

Later in the night he approached me and stared long into my face, as if wanting to commit to memory the picture of the man to whom he had disclosed the piercing secrets of his life. My mind was heavy with turmoil, my eyes with mist. He said quietly, "I am going now to walk through the night with the tempest, to feel the closeness of Nature's expression; it is a practise that I enjoy greatly in Autumn and Winter. Here is the wine, and there is the tobacco; please accept, my home as your own for the night."

He wrapped himself in a black robe and added smilingly, "I beg you to fasten the door against the intruding humans when you leave in the morning, for I plan to spend the day in the forest of the Holy Cedars." Then he walked toward the door, carrying a long walking staff and he concluded, "If the tempest surprises you again while you are in this vicinity, do not hesitate to take refuge in this hermitage... I hope you will teach yourself to love, and not to fear, the tempest. ...Good night, my brother."

He opened the door and walked out with his head high, into the dark. I stood at the door to see which course he had taken, but he had disappeared from view. For a few minutes I heard the fall of his feet upon the broken stones of the valley.

PART V

Morning came, after a night of deep thought, and the tempest had passed away, while the sky was clear and the mountains and the plains were revelling in the sun's warm rays. On my way back to the city I felt that spiritual awakening of which Yusif El Fakhri had spoken, and it was raging throughout every fibre of my being. I felt that my shivering must be visible. And when I calmed, all about me was beauty and perfection.

As soon as I reached the noisome people and heard their voices and saw their deeds, I stopped and said within myself, "Yes, the spiritual awakening is the most essential thing in man's life, and it is the sole purpose of being. Is not civilisation, in all its tragic forms, a supreme motive for spiritual awakening? Then how can we deny existing matter, while its very existence is unwavering proof of its conformability into the intended fitness? The present civilisation may possess a vanishing purpose, but the eternal law has offered to that purpose a ladder whose steps can lead to a free substance."

I never saw Yusif El Fakhr again, for through my endeavours to attend the ills of civilisation, Life had expelled me from North Lebanon in late Autumn of that same year, and I was required to live in exile in a distant country whose tempests are domestic. And leading a hermit's life in that country is a sort of glorious madness, for its society, too, is ailing.